TEST YOUR WITS!

TEST YOUR WITS!

Sheila Anne Barry

illustrated by **Doug Anderson**

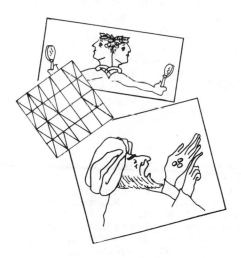

 Sterling Publishing Co., Inc.   New York

By the Same Author
Super-Colossal Book of Puzzles, Tricks & Games
Tricks & Stunts to Fool Your Friends
The World's Best Party Games
The World's Best Travel Games

Library of Congress Cataloging-in-Publication Data

Barry, Sheila Anne.
  Test your wits!

  Includes index.
  1. Puzzles.   I. Anderson, Doug, 1919–   I. Title.
GV1493.B32   1986   793.73   86-14483
ISBN 0-8069-4764-0
ISBN 0-8069-4765-9 (lib. bdg.)
ISBN 0-8069-4766-7 (pbk.)

Copyright © 1986 by Sterling Publishing Co., Inc.
Two Park Avenue, New York, N.Y. 10016
Distributed in Canada by Oak Tree Press Ltd.
% Canadian Manda Group, P.O. Box 920, Station U
Toronto, Ontario, Canada M8Z 5P9
Distributed in the United Kingdom by Blandford Press
Link House, West Street, Poole, Dorset BH15 1LL, England
Distributed in Australia by Capricorn Ltd.
P.O. Box 665, Lane Cove, NSW 2066
Manufactured in the United States of America

CONTENTS

PICTURE PUZZLES

gregory

Do you keep your wits about you? Do you really see what you're looking at? And make sense out of it? Do you remember it? You'll find out, with the picture puzzles in this chapter.

Sometimes you'll need to find an element that's missing. Sometimes you'll be looking for an object that's hidden. Sometimes you'll have to recall a scene or analyze what one group of creatures has in common. But in every case, you'll need to pay close attention—and look sharp!

The Garbles

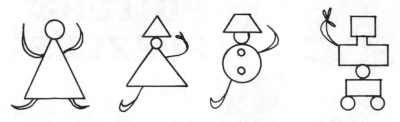

These are Garbles. All Garbles have something in common.

These are not Garbles.

Toots   **Nellie**   **Stacy**   **Duke**

Which ones are Garbles?

Answer on page 89.

Your Hidden Hosts

The owners of this house are very shy, and when guests show up, they hide. Can you find them?

Answer on page 89.

The Bermuda Rectangle

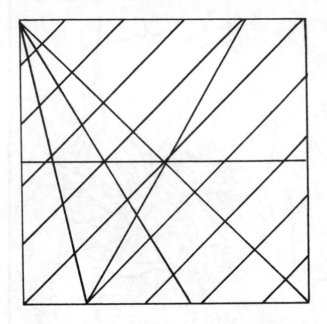

A rowboat has drifted into this peculiar atmospheric ecosphere—the Bermuda Rectangle. It is lost, perhaps forever, unless you can locate it. Can you?

The rowboat looks like this:

Answer on page 89.

The Farfels

These are Farfels. All Farfels have something in common.

These are not Farfels.

| **Sandy** | **Liz** | **Sasha** | **Pierre** |

Which ones are Farfels?

Answer on page 89.

The Crown of Zown

The archvillain Zoto has had his mind set on stealing the Crown of Zown for years. The king of Zown is trying to save it by distracting the eye of the onlooker with an arrangement of bars and posts. Will it work? Can you find the Crown of Zown?

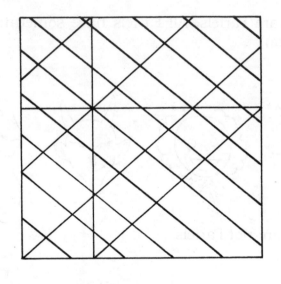

The Crown of Zown looks like this:

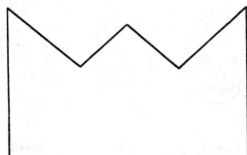

Answer on page 89.

The Traffic Accident

How good a witness are you? To test your ability to perceive and remember details, study the picture on this page for two minutes. Make only mental (no written) notes. Then turn the page and answer the questions without looking at this page again.

The Traffic Accident
(continued)

Allow yourself four minutes to answer the following questions about the accident. Then check your answers with the picture on page 13 and allow yourself one point for each answer that is essentially correct.

1. What was the date?
2. The approximate time?
3. Bus number?
4. What was the name of the taxi company?
5. Describe damage to taxi.
6. Could bus damage be described from your vantage point?
7. Did bus driver appear injured?
8. Describe apparent injuries to taxi driver.
9. Name on the ambulance?
10. In which direction was the taxi going?
11. In which direction was the bus going?
12. Describe the apparent point of impact.
13. Which vehicle struck the other?
14. What local news event was posted?
15. Name the newspaper building in the scene.
16. Name the hotel.
17. Describe the vehicle stopped behind the taxi.
18. Name the two streets at the intersection.
19. Name the shop at the intersection.
20. Give the license number of the bus.

See page 89 for an analysis of your score.

The Krippies

These are Krippies. All Krippies have something in common.

These are not Krippies.

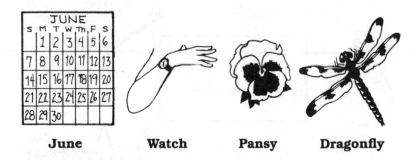

| **June** | **Watch** | **Pansy** | **Dragonfly** |

Which ones are Krippies?

Answer on page 89.

What's Missing?

In each picture below, one vital detail is missing. On a separate sheet of paper, list the missing items by number. Allow 3 minutes.

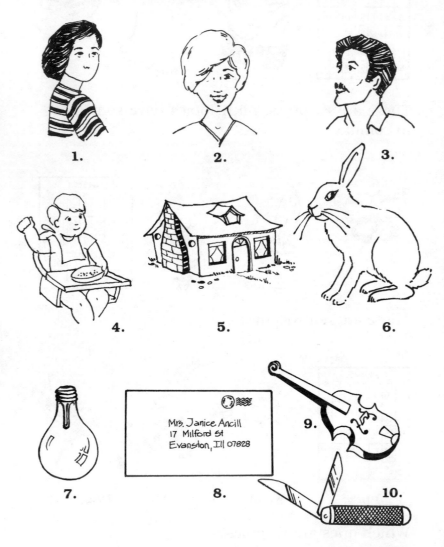

1.

2.

3.

4.

5.

6.

7.

8.

9.

10.

Mrs. Janice Ancill
17 Milford St
Evanston, Ill 07828

Answer on page 89.

Egg Fu Yong Vanishes

A container of Chinese food has disappeared in Mr. Lee's slick, neat, geometric livingroom. Mr. Lee is very hungry. Can you help him find it?

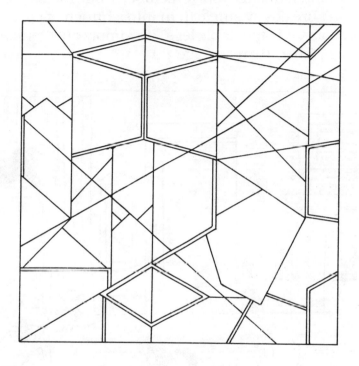

The Chinese food container looks like this:

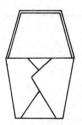

Answer on page 89.

Observation Test

Study the picture on this page for five minutes, but don't make any written notes. Then close the book and, on a separate sheet of paper, write down as many items as you remember from the scene. (Don't break any single item into a bunch of parts, such as table top, table legs. It's simply one item, a table.) Then turn to page 89.

See pages 89–90 for your score.

The Paraglops

These are Paraglops. All Paraglops have something in common.

These are not Paraglops.

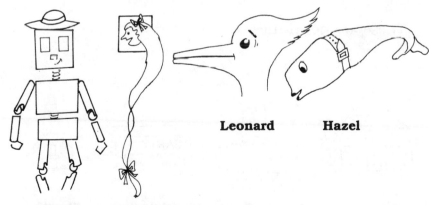

Leonard   **Hazel**

Ralphie   **Rapunzel**

Which ones are Paraglops?

Answer on page 89.

The Nifties

These are Nifties. All Nifties have something in common.

These are not Nifties.

The Oaks   Leffanoe's Castle   Charlie's Garage   Church

Which ones are Nifties?

Answer on page 90.

What's Missing This Time?

In each picture below, a vital detail is missing. On a separate sheet of paper, list the missing items by number. Allow 3 minutes.

1.

2.

3.

4.

5.

6.

7.

8.

9.

10.

Answer on page 90.

The Ribbles

These are Ribbles. All Ribbles have something in common.

These are not Ribbles.

Hepzibah   **Igor**   **The Baron**   **Mrs. Hyde**

Which ones are Ribbles?

Answer on page 90.

TEST YOUR APTITUDES AND ATTITUDES

In this section you'll not only test your memory, but you'll also get to try out other skills and abilities that you never thought about testing before. Are you a thorough person? A good organizer? Are you accurate and precise? Is your concentration good? How about your manual dexterity? Do you have a strong feeling for spatial relationships? Are you a good proofreader? How about your personality? What are you really like? If you didn't know about yourself before, here's your chance to find out!

Test Your Memory for Words

There are eight simple words in each of the four columns shown below. Working with one column at a time, read it aloud and then try to repeat the words in the right order silently to yourself. Read the column aloud again. Then immediately close the book and write as many of the words as you can remember—in their original order, if possible.

After you have finished doing this with each column, compare your list with the originals.

street	boy	hat	salt
light	desk	coat	pepper
lamp	school	shirt	stove
pole	chalk	shoes	pan
bank	blackboard	tie	water
clock	words	rack	sink
night	book	closet	faucet
policeman	teacher	door	drip

See page 90 for your score.

Test Your Memory for Shapes

Study the ten figures here for two minutes, trying to remember them so you'll recognize them when you see them again. Then turn the page for further instructions.

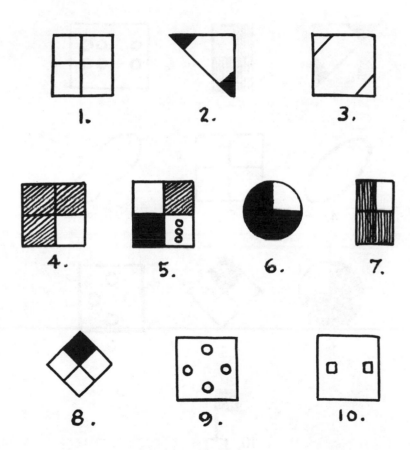

1.

2.

3.

4.

5.

6.

7.

8.

9.

10.

Test Your Memory for Shapes *(Continued)*

Some—but not all—of the shapes you studied on page 25 are repeated below. On a separate sheet of paper, list by number the ones you think are repeated. Then find out if you're right by checking back on page 25.

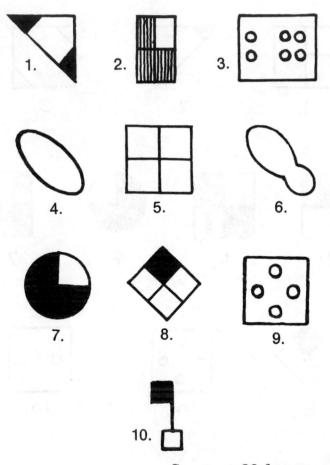

See page 90 for your score.

Are You a Good Organizer?

Each set of shapes below consists of geometrical parts that you can make into a perfect square. On a separate sheet of paper, draw these shapes so that they form that square. If you can visualize them easily and then put the parts together on paper, you're a good organizer. Allow five minutes.

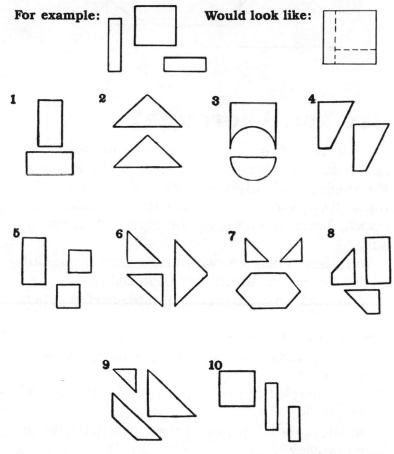

For example: **Would look like:**

1 2 3 4

5 6 7 8

9 10

Answer on page 90.

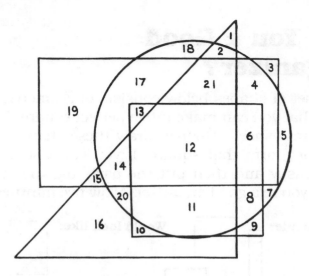

Are You Thorough?

Being thorough means paying attention to details and following instructions precisely. To test your thoroughness, study the figure that appears at the top of this page. Then answer the questions that appear below, referring to the figure when necessary.

Work fast! There's a two-minute time limit. But remember you're aiming for thoroughness.

Write your answers on a separate sheet of paper.

What numbers are:
1. In the triangle but not in the square, circle or rectangle?
2. In the circle but not in the square, triangle, or rectangle?
3. In the square but not in the circle, triangle, or rectangle?

4. In the rectangle but not in the circle, triangle, or square?
5. In both triangle and circle but not in the square or rectangle?
6. In both circle and square but not in the rectangle or triangle?
7. In both square and triangle but not in the rectangle or circle?

Are You Accurate?

In this test, you'll be looking at two sets of figures. Sometimes they're exactly the same, and sometimes they differ slightly. Working quickly, but as accurately as possible, jot down on a separate sheet of paper the key numbers of those pairs that are the *same*.

Allow 1½ minutes only. If you're not finished when your time is up, note the number at which you stopped.

1. 650	650	14. 36015992	360155992
2. 041	044	15. 3910066482	391006482
3. 2579	2579	16. 8510273301	8510273301
4. 3281	3281	17. 263136996	263136996
5. 55190	55102	18. 451152903	451152903
6. 39190	39190	19. 3259016275	3295016725
7. 658049	650849	20. 582039144	582039144
8. 3295017	3290517	21. 61558529	61588529
9. 63015991	63019991	22. 211915883	219915883
10. 39007106	39007106	23. 670413822	670143822
11. 69931087	69931087	24. 17198591	17198591
12. 251004818	251004418	25. 36482991	36482991
13. 299056013	299056013		

Answers on page 91.

Test Your Concentration

Concentration is the ability to disregard all other matters and focus your attention on a particular task. It is essential to constructive thinking. When you take the following tests, have the radio going, the TV set on, or provide some other distraction.

Concentrating on Numbers

Some people can concentrate more easily on numbers than on words or letters. In this first test, you'll find ten lines of numbers. In each line there is at least one (and sometimes more than one) pair of numbers next to each other whose sum is ten. For example: 2 6 4 7 1 5 0 3 7 8 2
              (6 + 4)   (3 + 7) (8 + 2)

List, on a separate sheet of paper, the pairs you can find in each line. Set up your answer like this: (6 + 4) (3 + 7) (8 + 2) = 3. You've got three minutes.

(a) 4 1 8 4 9 1 3 0 4 8 5 9 6 8 4 7 6 9 4 0 1 3 2 8 3 7 5 4 4 8

(b) 9 8 6 4 3 8 5 8 1 3 8 5 6 7 0 9 4 8 2 3 1 5 8 7 4 0 9 8 6 1

(c) 3 1 8 6 0 3 9 4 1 2 3 7 0 4 8 6 9 0 5 1 2 8 5 0 9 9 4 8 6 7

(d) 7 5 5 0 1 2 8 4 8 9 8 1 5 8 4 8 7 3 9 1 5 8 4 7 6 9 4 1 3 2

(e) 6 2 4 8 3 4 0 9 2 8 4 3 8 5 1 3 8 4 8 6 7 4 1 8 3 7 9 8 0 4

(f) 6 9 3 8 1 3 5 6 7 8 3 4 5 7 8 3 7 5 7 2 9 4 3 1 2 9 4 3 8 6

(g) 8 5 9 4 8 3 7 4 9 8 1 3 8 7 4 1 8 2 0 7 4 6 5 1 4 7 5 5 6 3

(h) 5 3 4 7 6 3 5 9 8 2 3 7 6 6 3 0 1 4 6 2 2 5 7 9 3 4 2 3 8 5

(i) 4 9 3 9 6 3 0 3 6 8 5 5 8 9 1 4 0 8 6 7 6 3 4 7 2 9 5 8 3 5

(j) 1 1 9 2 7 5 1 6 8 7 4 5 6 1 3 9 2 4 3 6 7 4 8 4 3 9 5 6 9 9

Answers on page 91.

Concentrating on Letters

In each of the ten lines of letters below, you'll find one or more letters next to each other that spell common words. For example:

P V T R A T Q O Y F X W

R A T

On a separate sheet of paper, list the words that you find, line by line. When you put the words together, they will form a meaningful sentence. Allow three minutes.

1. P T A O C I F N I J R Q T S E J L I U V T E W H X O L P Y O U
2. F R L D O J V U L H Q R C W E L L V X A G L T E F T H E X R C
3. C M I U V N T X E Z B J M I N O R V H I G T A S K S M J E J X
4. W H I C H A Q E V F R T I Y T H L D Y O U C N I J R N E Z E F
5. D L E Q G H T S V X A R E Z U I O C A L L E D E T J Q V N I R
6. X N I Q J E V K F F I H R D L J I Q H U I Y I H T L R U P O N
7. T O Q L R T S D E V H P E R F O R M I D X V Y O U M T Q W Z Z
8. B R W I L L L L J A Q H A V E W J H G B U T R J I A L I T T L E
9. E O C J D I F F I C U L T Y R D W I T H C J R Q A K S H L D U
10. V J B I Q T H E I U B J L I H V B I G G E R B L O N E S R Z X

Answer on page 91.

Are You Precise?

The idea in this test is to replace lines of numbers with unfamiliar symbols, actually to put the numbers into code. The code goes like this:

1	2	3	4	5	6	7	8	9
¯	И	⅃	L	U	◯	∧	x	=

Study the code for a few minutes. Then, on a separate sheet of paper, copy down the two lines of numbers shown below. Allow yourself 2½ minutes to write the correct symbol below each number.

Of course, you'll need to keep the book open in front of you as you work.

1 5 4 2 7 6 3 5 7 2 8 5 4 6 3 7 2 8 1 9 5 8 4 7 3
6 2 5 1 9 2 8 3 7 4 6 5 9 4 8 3 7 2 6 1 5 4 6 3 7

Are You Efficient?

Follow the same instructions as for the last test, "Are You Precise?" But this time, write the correct symbols for all three rows as quickly as you can, instead of observing a specific time limit. Time yourself carefully to determine how many seconds it takes you to complete the three rows. Remember to try for accuracy as well as speed.

3 1 2 1 3 2 1 4 2 3 5 2 9 1 4
6 3 1 5 4 2 7 6 3 8 7 2 9 5 4
6 3 7 2 8 1 9 5 8 4 7 3 6 9 5

Answer on page 91.

How Is Your Manual Dexterity?

Rule a sheet of paper into 150 half-inch (15-mm) squares (10 squares by 15).

Then, holding a sharpened pencil lightly in writing position, tap a dot into each square. Go from left to right in the top column, then from right to left in the second column, from left to right in the third, and so on. Don't stop to correct errors. Try to work as fast as you can while still being accurate.

Allow only 30 seconds.

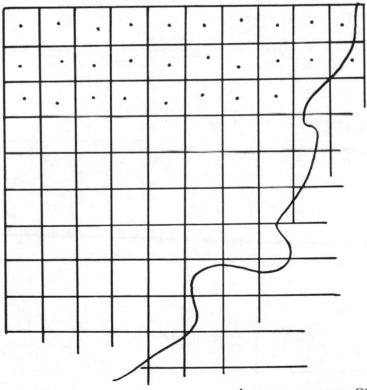

Answer on page 92.

Test Your Sense of Spatial Relationships

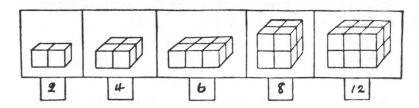

Take a look at the first row of cubes. The number beneath each box tells you how many cubes are contained in the box. Now figure out how many cubes are contained in each box below. You get three minutes.

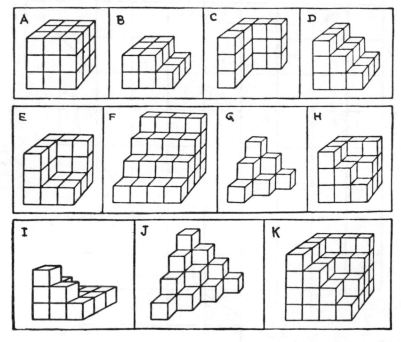

Answer on page 92.

Copyreading Aptitude Test

The lists below consist of 15 pairs of names. On some lines, the names are exactly alike. On other lines they're slightly different or errors appear. On a separate sheet of paper, list by number the lines containing one or more errors.

Allow 40 seconds for the test.

1. Sheppard Novelty Co.	Shepard Novelty Co.
2. Roberts and Lennon, Inc.	Roberts and Lennen, Inc.
3. Joseph Pape and Sons	Joseph Pape and Sons
4. Thompson Co.	Thompson, Inc.
5. Simplex Shoe Corp.	Simplex Shoe Corp.
6. Leibster & Bros.	Liebster & Bros.
7. Silver Standards Co.	Silver Standard Co.
8. Oppenheimer and Powers	Oppenheimer and Powers
9. Powers and Oppenheimers	Power and Oppenheimers
10. Northern Texas Petroleum	No. Texas Petroleum
11. Royaltone Corporation	Royalton Corporation
12. G. H. Furnath Co. Inc.	G. H. Furnath Co. Inc.
13. Harold Jacobsohn Co.	Herald Jacobsohn Co.
14. Terrell Express Co.	Terrill Express Co.
15. Hart Wallder and Sons	Hart Wallder and Sons

Answer on page 92.

Personality Tests

By the way people answer the questions on the innocent-looking tests that follow, you'll be able to tell them things about their personalities that will amaze them. The tests are silly and have nothing to do with psychology really, but they are fun to "give" to people and get them laughing and talking. Give them to yourself first and see what you "reveal" with your answers!

In a Dream Garden

1. Describe your dream garden.
2. Where is your house in relation to the garden?
3. What is the house like?
4. What is the key to your house like?
5. What would you do if you lost your key and wanted to get into your house?
6. You are standing alone holding something. What is it?

7. Near your garden is a house that belongs to someone else. It has a wall around it. There is a gate in the wall and a lock on the gate and you have no key for this lock. You want to get in. What would you do?

Walking in the Woods

You are walking through the woods when you come to a clearing. In the clearing, there is a lake. Beside the lake, there is a cup. You are thirsty.

1. What do you do:
    a. Use the cup to take a drink from the lake?
    b. Leave the cup where it is?
    c. Examine the cup in order to decide what to do?
2. Then do you—
    a. Put the cup back where it was?
    b. Leave it where it is?
    c. Take the cup away with you?

The water in the lake looks inviting. You are warm.

3. Do you—
    a. Wash your face and hands in it?
    b. Go swimming in it?
    c. Stay out of it?

You see a bear approaching as you stand by the lake. He is walking slowly and evidently doesn't see you.

4. Do you—
    a. Run as fast as you can?
    b. Stand very still?
    c. Try to make friends with the bear?

See page 92 for your analysis.

Are You an Extrovert or an Introvert?

An extrovert, according to the psychologists, is a person who is outgoing and sociable. They say that extroverts like people (though they usually don't have many really close friends), express themselves easily, enjoy parties and other social gatherings, and adjust to new situations easily. Their personalities are more on the outside, easy to get to know and understand.

The introvert's personality, on the other hand, is more on the inside. Introverts withdraw from social situations and live more with books and ideas than with fun and frolic. They are often sensitive and easily hurt, and generally it is harder for them to talk about their feelings. They have fewer friends than the extroverts, but the few they have may be close.

Very few people are completely one way or the other. "Extrovert" and "introvert" are actually ideas taken to the extremes—not people. Most people fall somewhere in between, having characteristics of both types.

Which is it better to be? It doesn't matter. Either one can be creative, brilliant, kind, constructive, lovable and fun. Sometimes, though, it's more convenient to be one type than another. If you have to go to a lot of parties, you'd enjoy it more if you were an extrovert. If you have to do a lot of reading, you'd be happier being an introvert.

But this kind of problem takes care of itself as you get older and you can choose the things you like to do. If you're an introvert, for example, you'd probably not even consider taking a job where you had to entertain people all the time and trying to sell them things. If you're an extrovert, you'd never try for a job that "made a hermit out of you." The question would just never come up.

Do extroverts have more fun? It depends on what you call fun. What is fun for the extrovert may be a bore to the introvert. An extrovert may have a splendid time making small talk all evening with a dozen people, when that could put an introvert to sleep. An introvert might have a perfectly marvelous time sitting with one close friend and listening to music, which might have an extrovert climbing the wall.

So now that you see that it makes absolutely no difference which you are—you'll see that it makes no sense at all to take the following test and find out.

Are You an Extrovert or an Introvert? *(continued)*

1. Do you always keep your promises, even when it's really difficult or unpleasant to keep them?
2. Do you get bored easily?
3. Do you often laugh out loud at funny movies?
4. Do you make up your mind about people quickly when you first meet them?
5. Do you usually climb stairs two at a time?
6. Do you like to do puzzles?
7. Do you pick your friends very carefully?
8. Do you like to ride on rollercoasters?
9. Do you shout or move around when you're watching a race or an important game?
10. Have you ever bought anything you had to save up for over a long period of time?
11. Do you have a bad temper?
12. Do you often leave things to the last minute?
13. Are you a dreamer?
14. Do you (or did you) occasionally play hookey from school?
15. Do you often rush to get somewhere, even if you have plenty of time?
16. Do you talk a lot when you're with a group of friends or at a party?
17. Will you take almost any dare?
18. Do you like to dance?
19. Do you often exaggerate when you tell your friends about something that happened?
20. Do you get very embarrassed if you have to make a speech?
21. Do you have to make a real effort to stay out of trouble?

22. Is it easy for you to talk about your feelings with members of your family?
23. Have you ever pretended to be sick in order to avoid a bad day at school or work?
24. Do you like to organize parties and get-togethers with your friends?
25. Do you have an easy time making friends with girls (if you're a girl) or boys (if you're a boy)?
26. Do you avoid crowds?
27. Do you often think about something so hard that you forget what's going on around you?
28. Are you shy?
29. Can you keep a secret?
30. Are you easily moved by a sad movie?
31. Do you often spend an evening just reading a book that has nothing to do with your school work?
32. Do you often get into trouble because you do things without thinking them through?
33. Do you usually eat faster than your friends, even when you're not in a hurry?
34. Do you walk faster than your friends?
35. Do you enjoy spending long periods of time alone?
36. Do you like to be doing something with your hands all the time, even when you're watching television?
37. Are you usually early for appointments?
38. Do you enjoy planning ahead?
39. Do you often think about God or why human beings were created?
40. Are you involved in many extracurricular activities?

See page 93 for your score.

WORD GAMES

In this section you'll find a few of the best word games ever invented. What's specially great about the ones here is that you can play them alone or with other people—anywhere, anytime and over and over again—without ever running out of challenges or getting bored.

Word Hunt

Take any word of about eight or ten letters and see how many words you can form from the letters in it, changing their order, of course. If a letter appears twice in the original word, you can use it twice to make words with it. If it appears only once, you can use it only once. For example, using the word H A P P I N E S S, you could make up such words as H A P P E N, but not P I P P I N.

No proper names or foreign words are allowed.

You can play the game with various rules. The most common rule is that words must have four or more letters. And it's not permitted to create a four-letter word by adding an "s" to a three-letter word.

You might want to make it really difficult by allowing words of only five or more letters.

If you're playing with other people, the winner is the one with the longest list. If you're playing alone, you can play against this book. Try the following words:

AMELIORATE	
Poor	0– 25
Fair	26– 50
Good	51– 80
Very Good	81–100
Excellent	over 100

CONSTRUCTION	
Poor	0–20
Fair	21–30
Good	31–45
Very Good	46–60
Excellent	over 60

DEVELOPING	
Poor	0–20
Fair	21–30
Good	31–40
Very Good	41–60
Excellent	over 60

ESTABLISH	
Poor	0–20
Fair	21–30
Good	31–40
Very Good	41–60
Excellent	over 60

IRREGULARLY		PRECIOUS	
Poor	0—15	Poor	0—15
Fair	16—25	Fair	16—25
Good	26—35	Good	26—35
Very Good	36—45	Very Good	36—45
Excellent	over 45	Excellent	over 45

Hint: It's easier to keep track of your words and not duplicate them if you set up your page by numbering down in the lefthand margin, and then starting each column of words with a different letter. See the sample page to the right.

	HAPPINESS				
1	happen	apse	pine	sane	nape
2	hasp	aspen	pane	sine	
3	hiss	ashen	pass	spine	
4			pain	shine	
5				snip	
6				snap	
7				spin	
8				shin	
9				ship	
10				shape	
11				snipe	

If you're testing yourself against this book, you'll find lists of 4-and-more letter words on pages 93—95. Allow yourself 10 minutes for each hunt, 1 point for each word.

See pages 93—95 for word lists.

Crosswords to Go

All you need to play this word game is paper and pencil and some way to select 25 different letters of the alphabet. You could use anagrams, if you have them, or tiles from a word game or just write out the alphabet on a sheet of paper.

Once you have your alphabet set up, draw a grid on the sheet of paper like the ones below. The grid should be made up of six lines in each direction, giving you 5 boxes horizontally and five boxes vertically.

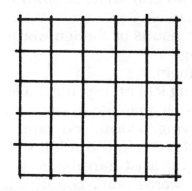

Then pick a letter. If you have anagrams or letter tiles, shake them up and pick one. If you've written out the alphabet, shut your eyes, spin the page around and then point to one of the letters with your pencil. Whatever letter you get you have to write into one of those little boxes. You pick which one.

Now pick another letter. And write that one in, too. And then another, until you've packed 25 letters and filled all the boxes.

How do you know where to write them? You

don't. You just try to put each letter in the place where it will help you to spell out the maximum number of words in any—or every—direction. The best you could hope to get would be ten five-letter words, but that is practically impossible if you select the letters at random and play the game according to these rules:

1. Be sure to write down each letter before you select the next one.
2. If a letter comes up twice, you can use it again. But you can only write it down once for each appearance.
3. No proper nouns or foreign words.
4. No erasing.
5. No rearranging.
6. No skipping letters. If you get a letter that you can't possibly manage to work into the words you are trying to form, you have to put it down anyway wherever you think it will do the most good—or the least harm!
7. Two-letter words don't count, but three-letter words do. Example: If you have s-e-p-a-r and want to make S-P-E-A-R out of them, you can't. But you can count the 3-letter word "par" as one of your words. If you have S-U-N-A-P, you can count either "sun" or "nap," but not both.
8. Score 10 points for a 5-letter word, 5 points for a 4-letter word and 3 points for a 3-letter word.
9. If you're playing against an opponent, you don't need to use anagrams or tiles or even write out the alphabet. Just take turns calling out the letters you'd like to use! You can be sure of one thing: you and your opponent won't

want the same letters, and your choices will drive each other crazy. Especially if you try to give tough letters like K or X late in the game when they will give your opponent the worst jolt.

Twin Crosswords to Go

Play with two grids at the same time. Playing this way, you get to choose which square you'll put each each letter in. Easier? Not really!

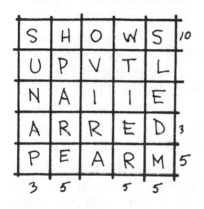

The same letters can give you 36 points— or 66!

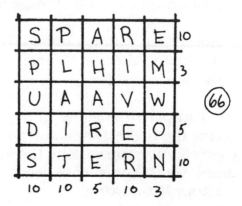

Categories

Are you a list-maker? If so, this ultimate list game is what you've been waiting for.

On the following pages are the rules for four different categories:

Boys' Names

Girls' Names

Animals

Food Plants

What you need to do is write down every item you can think of that fits into the list you're working on. Let's say you pick *Animals*. First read the rules of the category. Then write down every animal you can think of that begins with A, then with B, and so on through the alphabet. If you can come up with at least one animal for every letter, you get an automatic bonus score of 200 points. Then look at the list on pages 120 through 123 and find the number ratings for all the animal names you wrote down. For example, *Ape* is worth only one point, because it is such a familiar creature. But *Anoa* would be worth 10 points, because it is little known. Then see how you made out, with the Rating Chart on the "rules," page 51.

Note: Keep your list divided by letter, so that all A's are together, all B's, etc. It is easier to score that way.

You can play this game in a group and see who scores the highest, or alone and compete against yourself. After you've done the same category a few times, you become an expert.

Happy list-making!

Boys' Names

See the instructions for Categories on page 48.

This is an almost endless category, and you'll find more names than you care to know about in the list on pages 102–111. Many rare names have been left out for space purposes. If you come up with a name which does not appear in the list in the book, and it is:

(1) in a name book or
(2) in the dictionary or
(3) known to you because you know someone by that name, or
(4) accepted by the group,

give yourself 10 points for it. Do *not* give yourself 10 points if the name is pronounced exactly the same way as another name which is listed—but spelled differently. Give yourself the number of points for the name that sounds the same. Foreign names *are* allowed.

Allow yourself half an hour to make up your list.

BONUS: For a bonus of 200 points, you must come up with a name for every letter of the alphabet.

Rating Chart

Over 200	Excellent
175–200	Very Good
150–175	Good
125–150	Fair
Below 125	Poor

See word list on pages 102–111.

Girls' Names

See the instructions for Categories on page 48.

Here is another category that goes on and on. Again, many rare names have been left out for space purposes. If you come up with a name that does not appear in the list and it is

(1) in a name book or
(2) in the dictionary or
(3) known to you because you know someone by that name, or
(4) accepted by the group

give yourself 10 points for it. Do not give yourself 10 points if the name is pronounced exactly the same way as another name which is listed—but spelled differently. Give yourself the number of points for the name that sounds the same. Foreign names *are* allowed.

Allow yourself half an hour to make up your list.

BONUS: For a bonus of 200 points, you must come up with a name for every letter of the alphabet.

Rating Chart

Over 200	**Excellent**
175—200	**Very Good**
150—175	**Good**
125—150	**Fair**
Below 125	**Poor**

See word list on pages 112—120.

Land Animals—Mammals

See the instructions for Categories on page 48.

All the animals listed in this category are mammals. No birds or insects, fishes or marine mammals are included. The list does not include breeds of dogs or cats, either. If you come up with the name of an animal that does not appear in the list on pages 120–123, and it is

(1) in the dictionary
(2) in some other reference work
(3) agreed to by the group, if you are playing this game at a party, give yourself 10 points for it. Any mammal on earth is fair game.

Allow yourself about 20 minutes to make up your list.

BONUS: In this category, give yourself a bonus of 200 points for a complete alphabet, even if you don't have an animal name for U, Q or X.

Rating Chart

Over 100	**Excellent**
70–100	**Very Good**
50– 70	**Good**
30– 50	**Fair**
Below 30	**Poor**

See word list on pages 120–123.

Food Plants

See the instructions for Categories on page 48.

If it grows and is eaten—or used to spice other foods—it belongs in this list. Here you'll find fruits and vegetables, grains and nuts and herbs from all over the world. If you come up with an edible plant that does not appear in the list and it is

(1) in the dictionary or
(2) in some other reference work or
(3) accepted by the group

give yourself 10 points for it.

Allow yourself 20 minutes to make up your list.

BONUS: In this category, give yourself a bonus of 200 points for a complete alphabet even if you don't have a plant name for the letter U.

Rating Chart

Over 100	Excellent
70–100	Very Good
50–70	Good
30–50	Fair
Under 30	Poor

See word list on pages 123–126.

TRIVIA QUIZZES

Here are quizzes that you can use in many different ways. Each one is divided into 3 sections:

2 point questions which are relatively easy
3 point questions which are more difficult
5 point questions which are pretty hard

You can use them for trivia games, make up your own quiz games, played under your own rules, or test your own knowledge and keep score. For example, the highest possible score on five quizzes is 200 points (40 per quiz). A score of 110 or better is good; a score of 153 or more is excellent.

Literature Quiz

Two-Point Questions

1. In a novel Robert Louis Stevenson wrote in 1896, young David Balfour is sent to sea by a cruel uncle. Was that book *Kidnapped* or *Treasure Island*?
2. Getting nowhere as a playwright, this French writer switched to science-fiction 100 years ago and wrote *20,000 Leagues under the Sea* and *From the Earth to the Moon*. Who was he?
3. In the 17th century, Cervantes wrote a book in which a poor country squire, crazed by the idea of chivalry, carried his enthusiasm for it to such a point that the excessive chivalry of the times was soon laughed out of favor. Name that book.
4. What did the soothsayer warn Julius Caesar to beware of?

Three-Point Questions

1. In 1516, Sir Thomas More wrote a book about an imaginary land where people lived in great peace and happiness under pure socialism. From the title, we added a word to our language to characterize any scheme which is too visionary and impractical. Name the book.
2. Name the book written by an English tinker during his years in prison at Bedford for "unlawful" preaching. His name was John Bunyan.
3. Name the King involved in Tennyson's "Idylls of the King."
4. Thanks to re-runs of old movies on TV, you may know that William Bendix starred in *The Hairy Ape*. But who wrote the play on which the movie was based?

Five-Point Questions

1. In Sheridan's play, *The Rivals*, one of the female characters constantly confuses words that are similar in sound but different in meaning (for instance, saying "Allegories are things that live on river banks"). Her name has become identified with such mistakes. What is it?

2. An obscure pirate named Alexander Selkirk was marooned for four years on a South Pacific island. A great English author based a fictional book on Selkirk's experiences there. Name the book and the author.

3. A novel by Nathaniel Hawthorne relates a story of the persecution of Clifford Pyncheon by his cousin, Judge Pyncheon—but Clifford and his sister Hepzibah find peaceful years when the Judge dies. Hawthorne named the book after the home in which Clifford and Hepzibah lived. Give its title.

4. The longest sentence in literature runs for forty pages! It is spoken by a character named Molly Bloom. Name the novel and the author.

Answers on page 95.

"Bad Guys" Quiz

Two-Point Questions

1. This Roman emperor had his own mother executed, murdered his wife, killed a girl who wouldn't marry him, and then put many Christians to death after accusing them of burning Rome. What was his name?
2. This Sioux Indian chief headed the Indian forces that massacred General Custer's men. Name him.
3. This miserly character hated the Christmas spirit until Christmas ghosts reformed him. Who was he?
4. This King of the Huns was so cruel in warfare that he was called "The Scourge of God." However, when he ravaged Italy in 452 A.D., Pope Leo I persuaded him to spare Rome. Name him.

Three-Point Questions

1. Othello has become the symbol of all overly jealous husbands. But who was the villain whose

insinuations drove Othello to murder Desdemona?

2. This pirate had his headquarters on an island off Louisiana. He pillaged shipping in the Gulf of Mexico. However, for helping General Jackson at the Battle of New Orleans, he was pardoned by President Madison but soon went back to piracy! What was his name?

3. In Dickens' *Oliver Twist*, what was the name of the unscrupulous old man who taught young boys to become thieves and pickpockets?

4. In the short story by Stephen Vincent Benet, against whom did Daniel Webster contend for the unfortunate Jabez Stone?

Five-Point Questions

1. In *Les Miserables*, Jean Valjean was persecuted and hounded by an overzealous detective. Name him.

2. Name the general who, in Richard Connell's famous short story, "The Most Dangerous Game," lived on a Caribbean island (alone except for his huge servant, Ivan) and hunted helpless men whom he lured to the island as "game" for his hunting sport.

3. Name the Italian statesman who wrote *The Prince*, a book based on the theory that maintenance of power justifies deceit and treachery in government.

4. As Spanish governor of the Netherlands in the 16th century, this tyrant executed over 18,000 people to maintain order. Later he conquered Portugal with the same brutality. He had the title of Duke. Name him.

Answers on page 95.

Mythology Quiz

Two-Point Questions
1. Who was the Roman god of love?
2. When he made his trip to Colchis, what was Jason in quest of?
3. Who performed twelve great labors?
4. On what mountain did the Greek gods live?

Three-Point Questions
1. Name the man-eating, one-eyed shepherds who, according to Homer, dwelt in Sicily.
2. Who finally cut the Gordian knot with one stroke of his sword?
3. Which handsome youth fell in love with his own reflection in a pool and was changed into a flower that bears his name?
4. Name the Roman god whose two heads faced in opposite directions.

Five-Point Questions
1. The ancient Greeks had a myth about an animal, born from the blood of Medusa, that rode through the sky at will. Identify and name that animal.
2. The staff of Hermes, herald of the gods, has become the symbol of physicians. Name it.

3. Name the boatman who ferried the dead across a river in Hell.
4. Name the father-and-son team who learned to fly on wings of feathers and wax invented by the father.

Answers on pages 95–96.

Legends, Tales and Fables Quiz

Two-Point Questions
1. Who was the merry chaplain of Robin Hood's band?
2. Name the triangular stone at an old Irish castle that gives the gift of a glib tongue to all who kiss it.
3. Which famous sailor hitched a ride out of the Valley of Diamonds on a fabulous bird called a roc?
4. Who was Tom Sawyer's best pal?

Three-Point Questions
1. Name the Three Musketeers in the novel of that name.
2. Name the imaginary monster in *Through the Looking-Glass*.
3. Name the fabulous Arabian bird that dies, burns itself to ashes, and then rises to new life from its own ashes.
4. Name the boy hero of *Treasure Island*.

Five-Point Questions

1. A Norse myth tells of two children who were kidnapped by the moon while drawing water. Under what names did they turn up in nursery rhymes?
2. Name the sculptor of Greek legend who fell in love with his own statue of Aphrodite, whereupon the goddess gave the statue life and he married her!
3. Attila the Hun was called the Scourge of God, but which conqueror was called the Nightmare of Europe?
4. Which nephew of King Arthur seized the kingdom in Arthur's absence? On his return, Arthur killed this nephew but was mortally wounded in the combat.

Answers on page 96.

Famous People Quiz

Two-Point Questions

1. Who was the "Lady of the Lamp" who founded modern nursing?
2. This famous American poet wrote "Leaves of Grass."

3. Legend says that a falling apple gave this mathematician the idea of the Law of Gravity.
4. In silent movie days, she was known as "America's Sweetheart."

Three-Point Questions
1. Accused of corrupting the youth of Athens, this Greek philosopher was compelled to drink a poisonous cup of hemlock.
2. This hated king of England was forced to sign the Magna Carta.
3. This great Italian sculptor and goldsmith wrote his autobiography.
4. This Portuguese navigator discovered what Columbus failed to find: the sea route from Europe to India (by way of the Cape of Good Hope).

Five-Point Questions
1. Name the German scientist who discovered X-rays.
2. This Italian artist often painted hair in a rich red tone.
3. Name the German socialist who collaborated with Karl Marx in helping complete *Das Kapital*.
4. These twin brothers, from Belgium, became famous for their balloon ascents and bathysphere descents. What is their surname?

Answers on page 96.

Bible Quiz

Two-Point Questions
1. Name the Philistine giant whom David slew.
2. Who was the cousin and forerunner of Jesus who called on the people to prepare for the Mesiah?
3. Name the most sacred city of Palestine.
4. Name the prophet who was swallowed by a great fish.

Three-Point Questions
1. Name the large fresh-water lake, in the upper region of Palestine, which is closely associated with the ministry of Jesus.
2. Name the "father" of the Hebrews.
3. What was the name of Paul before his conversion to Christianity?
4. In their conquest of Canaan, the Israelites took a large city by marching around it and blowing their trumpets. Name the city and tell what happened there.

Five-Point Questions
1. Name the three sons of Noah.

2. After serving his Uncle Laban for seven years in order to marry one of his uncle's daughters, Jacob was given a daughter he didn't want and married her. However, by serving another seven years, he won the wife he originally desired. Name each of these wives.
3. What official title did Pontius Pilate have?
4. How many years is Methuselah supposed to have lived?

Answers on page 96.

Interesting Places

Two-Point Questions
1. Which continent is called the Dark Continent?
2. Which continent is really a large island?
3. On which continent did Western culture arise?
4. Name the extensive mountain system in Europe which forms a 15,000-foot-high border between France and Switzerland.

Three-Point Questions
1. Do most of the earth's land masses lie north or south of the Equator?
2. The deepest trough in the earth's surface lies near the island of Mindanao in the Philippines (35,400 feet deep). Name the mountain range which constitutes the *highest* upward thrust in the earth's surface.

3. Is the North Pole a land area or an ocean area?
4. Name the sea which Columbus thoroughly explored on his last three visits to America.

Five-Point Questions
1. Name the wide, beautiful street along the waterfront in Shanghai.
2. Give the number of the famous U.S. Route which connects Chicago with Los Angeles.
3. Name the most famous of the old Roman highways, connecting Rome with Brindisi.
4. Name the island in the Pacific Ocean, 2,000 miles off Chile, where hundreds of huge, partly finished, monolithic statues pose one of the great mysteries of archeology.

Structures — Where Are They?

Two-Point Questions
1. The Parthenon.
2. The Great Sphinx.
3. The Colosseum.
4. Westminster Abbey.

Three-Point Questions
1. The Taj Mahal.
2. The Pantheon.
3. The Alhambra.
4. St. Mark's Cathedral.

Five-Point Questions
1. The Mosque of St. Sophia.
2. The Duomo.
3. The Escorial.
4. Mosque of Omar.

Answers on pages 96–97.

Rivers — Volcanoes
Where Are They?

Two-Point Questions
1. Hwang Ho.
2. Yukon.
3. Danube.
4. Rio Grande.

Three-Point Questions
1. Brahmaputra.
2. Don.
3. Fraser.
4. Oder.

Five-Point Questions
1. Mekong.
2. Yenisei.
3. Murray.
4. Parnaiba.

Two-Point Questions
1. Mt. Vesuvius.
2. Fujiyama.
3. Mauna Loa.
4. Popocatepetl.

Three-Point Questions
1. Lassen Peak.
2. Paricutin.
3. Mt. Etna.
4. Kilimanjaro.

Five-Point Questions
1. Asosan.
2. Krakatoa.
3. Wrangell.
4. Colima.

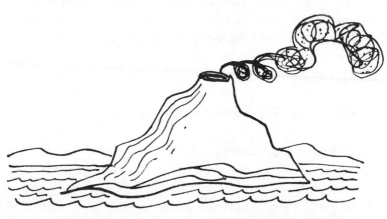

Answers on page 97.

Nursery Rhymes Quiz

Two-Point Questions

1. When Polly put the kettle on, what was in it?
2. How old was the pease porridge in the pot?
3. What did Little Jack Horner pull out?
4. Where was Little Boy Blue?

Three-Point Questions

1. For what three people did the black sheep have his three bags of wool?
2. What did the Old Woman Who Lived in a Shoe give her children?
3. Monday's child is fair of face. What is Tuesday's child?
4. What did Simple Simon go fishing for?

Five-Point Questions

1. What was the only tune that Tom the Piper's Son could play?
2. When Bobby Shaftoe went to sea, what did he have on his knee?

3. What did Wee Willie Winkie cry as he ran through the town?
4. What did Old Mother Goose ride on when she wanted to wander?

Answers on page 97.

Who Are They in the Movies?

Two-Point Questions
1. Norma Jean Baker
2. Archibald Leach
3. Marion Michael Morrison
4. Frances Gumm

Three-Point Questions
1. Name the dance team: Virginia McMath and Frederick Austerlitz
2. Name the famous "feuders": Benjamin Kubelsky and John F. Sullivan
3. Name the popular comedy team of the 50's: Joseph Levitch and Dino Crocetti
4. What kind of movies did the following actors make? William Pratt and Laszlo Loewenstein

Five-Point Questions
What do they have in common?
1. David Daniel Kaminsky
   Nathan Birnbaum
   Mendel Berlinger
   Melvin Kaminsky
   William Claude Dukinfield

2. Harlean Carpentier
   Maria Magdalena von Losch
   Margarita Carmen Cansino
   Camille Javal
   Sophia Scicoloni

3. Doris Kappelhoff
   Caroline Blanauer
   Vito Farinola
   Nathaniel Coles
   Nick Perido

4. Sean O'Feeney
   David Wark
   Michael Igor Peschkowsky
   Mihaly Kertesz
   Allen Stewart Konigsberg

Answers on pages 97–98.

THE GREAT BRAINTEASERS

The brainteasers in this chapter are classic puzzles that have been baffling people for centuries. Some of them appear in modern dress, but don't be fooled—they are older than any of us and most of them are trickier than they look!

The Pufferbill in the Pear Tree

A pufferbill, a shaggy bird from the faraway planet Zuto, was captured by a space team and brought down to earth. Not knowing what the pufferbill would like to eat, earth scientists placed it in a special experimental cage stocked with different types of fruit trees. They watched as the pufferbill flew from tree to tree. Finally, it settled on a pear tree, sampled one of the leaves and flapped its wings in incredulous delight. That first day it ate several leaves. The second day, it ate twice as much. The next day it doubled its intake once again. And so it went for 30 days, till only the fruit remained on the tree: the pufferbill had devoured all the leaves!

Can you figure out on what day half the leaves were gone?

Answer on page 98.

New Year's Resolution

Suppose you made a New Year's resolution to save twice as much each day as you did the day before, starting with a penny a day. On January 1st, you would save one penny; on January 2nd, you would save 2 pennies; on January 3rd, you would save 4 pennies; on January 4th you would save 8 pennies. At the end of January, how many pennies would you have saved?

First try to guess the answer without figuring it out mathematically.

If you don't have a calculator, look up the answer on page 98.

Cross-Country Tour

You are about to start on a 12,000-mile (19,200 km) auto trip across the country. You are told by your mechanic that your four tires definitely will last 8,000 miles (12,800 km) each, but not a mile more. You can't take any chances, so you have to buy some spares and carry them with you. How many spare tires do you need to buy?

Death Meets the Squire

In a small English town long ago, this story was told:

It was a hot summer Sunday. The squire and his wife were in church when the squire fell asleep. He dreamed he was a French nobleman at the time of the Revolution. He had been condemned to death, and he was waiting on the scaffold for the guillotine to fall. Just then his wife, noticing that he was asleep, tapped him sharply on the back of his neck with her fan. The shock was so great—in view of what he was dreaming—that the squire immediately slumped over, dead.

Could this story be true? Why?

Answer on page 98.

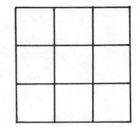

Magic Fifteen

Fill the squares with numbers from 1–9, no number being used twice. The numbers must add up to 15 in all directions—horizontally in all three rows, vertically in all three rows, as well as the two diagonals.

Send More Money

SEND
+ MORE
MONEY

Besides being a message you'd like to send, this is a famous numerical cryptogram. Each letter stands for a number, and no number has been used for more than one letter. Can you decipher it?

Famous 45

Divide the number 45 into four parts so that if 2 is added to the first and subtracted from the second, if the third is multiplied by 2 and the fourth divided by 2, the result of each process will be the same.

Answers on pages 98–99.

Dividing the Loaves

This puzzle has been stumping the unwary since Biblical times. The legend goes that many years ago, two Arabs were travelling to Baghdad and stopped at a small town for a meal. One of the Arabs had five loaves of bread in his camel-sack, and the other Arab had three loaves.

Before they began eating, they were joined by a hungry stranger who asked for food and offered to pay for what he ate. The two Arabs agreed to divide their bread with him, so he sat down and ate. They divided the bread equally, and when the meal was over, the stranger laid down eight coins of equal value in payment for the food. He said good-bye and went on his way.

The Arab who had had five loaves took five of the coins as his share, and the other Arab was left with three. The second Arab was not pleased with this division and argued that he should receive half of the coins. The two Arabs couldn't agree on this, and they argued so vehemently that finally they had to take their case to a judge.

The judge listened to the story of what had happened, and then he said, "The man who had five loaves should receive seven of the coins, and the man who had three loaves should receive only one."

Which is the correct division of the coins? Remember, the coins are of *equal* value.

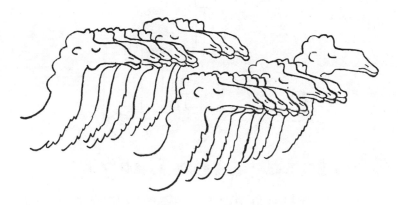

Dividing the Camels

Many years ago an Egyptian died and left his estate, which consisted of seventeen camels, to his three sons. The eldest son was left half of the camels, the second son was left a third of the camels, and the youngest son was to receive one-ninth of the camels, according to the will.

The sons and their legal advisers could figure no way to make the distribution without cutting up a camel. So they went to the Pharaoh for advice. The Pharaoh, after listening to the problem, thought for a moment and then announced a solution which had not occurred to anyone. What was it?

Answers on page 99.

Who Is the Avon Lady?

Jill, Tracy and Liz each work at two jobs. Each one of them is two of the following: actress, model, private detective, sculptor, race car driver and Avon lady.

From these facts, can you tell which girl is the Avon lady? And which is involved in each of the other occupations?

1. The sculptor and the race car driver used to go to school with Jill.
2. The model bought some make-up from the Avon lady.
3. Liz beat both Tracy and the model at tennis.
4. The actress and the sculptor are roommates.
5. The actress dated the model's brother.
6. Tracy owes the race car driver $10.

Answer on page 99.

What Is the Name of the Largest Rabbit in the World?

Jim, Mark and Sally each have unusual pets. Jim calls his Jarvis, Mark calls his Marvin, and Sally calls hers Spot. One of the pets is a baboon, another is a penguin, and the third is the largest rabbit in the world.

1. The rabbit played soccer with his owner yesterday.
2. Jim's leg has been in a cast for 2 months.
3. The baboon's owner goes horseback riding every Saturday with one of the other pet lovers.
4. The baboon bit Marvin.

What is the name of the largest rabbit in the world?

Answer on page 99.

African Thinking Game

An explorer goes to Africa to find his friend Diamala, but he doesn't know what tribe Diamala belongs to. There are three tribes in the area, the Elephant Tribe, the Leopard Tribe and the Crocodile Tribe.

A person belonging to the Elephant Tribe always tells the truth.

A person belonging to the Leopard Tribe always lies.

A person belonging to the Crocodile Tribe sometimes tells the truth but sometimes lies.

In order to find his friend Diamala, the explorer must find out what tribe Diamala belongs to. He asks three Africans—each from a different tribe—two questions: "What tribe to you belong to? What tribe does Diamala belong to?"

Agassu answers: "I am not an Elephant. Diamala is a Leopard."

Bantu says, "I am not a Leopard. Diamala is a Crocodile."

Coffi says, "I am not a Crocodile. Diamala is an Elephant."

What tribe does Agassu belong to? What tribe does Bantu belong to? What tribe does Coffi belong to? And finally, what tribe does Diamala belong to?

Answer on pages 99–100.

The Mailbox Mystery

The vice-president of a large corporation had an extremely efficient housekeeper. When he left for his vacation, he instructed her to forward the mail to him at his camp. During July he received no mail, so he phoned his home and asked the housekeeper what had happened. She explained that he had forgotten to leave her the mailbox key.

The vice-president apologized and promised to mail her the key right away. During August, he still received no mail, though the housekeeper told him there was a batch of mail in the box. When he returned home, he immediately fired the house-keeper. Was he right in doing this? Or was he unfair? Why?

Answers on page 100.

The Two Brothers

A Saxon king, displeased with the greed shown by his two sons, left a will with an unusual provision: The sons were to mount their horses in a tiny town on the border of the kingdom and ride, without dismounting more than once, to the gate of the king's castle. The son whose horse arrived *second* at the castle gate was to be awarded the entire fortune.

When the king passed away, the sons began their "race," moving along slowly together for days on end. Each tried to go slower than the other and after a while, they got so sleepy they had to dismount and get some sleep at an inn. While they slept, they each had their footmen alerted to notify them when the other left the inn. Actually, they left the inn together. As they were about to mount their horses, one brother whispered a few words to the other, they both laughed, jumped into the saddles and raced the horses as fast as they could to the castle gate.

It doesn't matter to us which brother won the fortune, but can you figure out what the brother whispered?

Cannibals and Missionaries

This classical puzzle has stumped people for many years. Possibly it is based on a real event.

In deepest Africa there once were three missionaries who had converted three cannibals and were bringing them back to civilization. When they reached the Congo River, they realized they would have a problem ferrying the cannibals across, because their boat could carry only two at a time. It was not safe to let the cannibals outnumber the missionaries at any time—not on either side of the river nor in the boat. To complicate matters further, only one of the cannibals, the king, could row, although all three missionaries could handle the boat.

Using pencil and paper—or coins—or toothpicks—can you figure out how many trips it took them to get across safely?

Answers on page 100.

The Wise King

During the Middle Ages, a Nordic king was writing his will. His sons were good friends, and the king wanted to make sure that they would have no cause for jealousy after his death over the division of his property. He didn't want to provide in his will merely that the possessions were to be divided equally, lest his sons start quarrelling over what each was to get.

Finally the king thought of a foolproof yet simple way of providing for absolutely equal distribution of his possessions. What did he write in his will?

The Casket and the Basket

Perhaps not as ancient as some of the puzzles in this section, but old enough, is this story of the royal family imprisoned in London Tower. The king (who weighed 200 pounds [100 kg]), the queen (who weighed 110 pounds [55 kg]) and the crown prince (who weighed 95 pounds [47.5 kg]) were all imprisoned in the tower, along with a casket (weighing 80 pounds [40 kg] filled) which contained the royal jewels. Some of their friends managed to rig up a pulley with two baskets and a rope long enough to reach from the tower window to the ground.

Word reached the prisoners that they were going to be moved to another prison the next day, so the king decided to get his family out by the pulley and baskets that very night. He knew that the pulley arrangement would work just so long as there was no more than 15 pounds (7.5 kg) difference in weight between the two baskets.

The king put the casket in one basket, lowered it to the ground, and ordered the crown prince to get into the other basket. Did the royal family manage to escape with their lives and their jewels? If so, how did they do it? Even a mechanical engineer may have trouble with this one!

Note: Actually 1 kilo (kg) = about 2.2 pounds, but in the metric version of this puzzle, the royal family and its jewels are a little heavier.

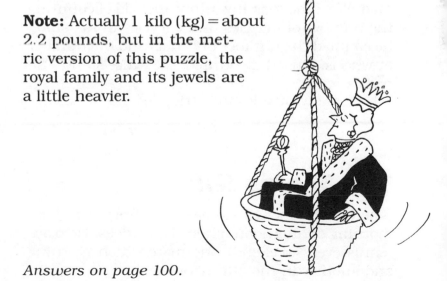

Answers on page 100.

Madness at the Bike Shop

The owner of the Atlantis Bicycle Shop was quite mad. When he took inventory, instead of counting the number of bicycles and tricycles in his store, he counted the number of pedals and the number of wheels. Once he counted 153 wheels and 136 pedals.

How many bicycles and tricycles did he have?

Answer on page 100.

The Tennis Nut

Whenever Rodney can sneak away from work for a morning or afternoon of tennis, he does. He plays tennis every weekend: one match each morning and another in the afternoon.

Since the beginning of July he went to work 26 days, but never for the whole day. On these days he played tennis either in the morning or in the afternoon.

Up to last night, he played 25 matches in the morning and 21 in the afternoon.

Rodney is going to be fired on August 6th. How much time does he have?

Answer on page 101.

The Mutilated Dictionary

Mark's dictionary had 632 pages. Each page had 25 entries and every seventh entry was illustrated. One day, when he went to use his dictionary, Mark found that his little sister had cut out all the illustrations which were among the first five and the last six entries on each page.

Can you tell how many illustrations remained in Mark's mutilated dictionary?

Answer on page 101.

Revolution in Platonia

After the revolution in Platonia, the dethroned king, his prime minister, and his treasurer were arrested and tried by the revolutionary court. Before sentence was passed, the judge spoke to each of the prisoners.

To the king he said, "If *and only if* both your ministers receive the same sentence will you be executed."

To the prime minister, he said "If *and only if* the king and the treasurer receive the same sentence will you be imprisoned."

To the treasurer, the judge said, "If *and only if* the other two receive different sentences will you be set free."

The judge then pronounced his sentence. "Tomorrow morning one of you will be set free, another will be imprisoned for life, and the third will be executed." He then ordered the guards to lead the prisoners away.

"Wait!" they shouted, "what's to become of us?"

The judge merely replied, "I've already told you," and he walked calmly away. What were the respective sentences?

Russian Tunnel

During World War II, three Russian V.I.P.'s, Molotov, Vishinsky and Malenkov, were travelling on a train in Russia. Suddenly the train entered a tunnel without the conductor's turning on the lights. The tunnel was long and sooty. At the moment the train emerged, Stalin wandered into the car and noticed that the men had become spotted with soot.

He said to them: "Before I show you a mirror, I have an idea. Your answers will show me which of you is the quickest thinker."

The three men immediately sat up and paid strict attention, for each was anxious to show Stalin how smart he was.

"Now," said Stalin, "each of you gentlemen will please look at the other two, and if you see *one* whose forehead is smudged with soot, raise your hand."

All three quickly raised their hands.

Stalin continued, "As soon as any one of you knows with certainty whether he himself has been smudged or not, drop your hand."

Looking at each other for a few moments, the three men kept their hands raised. Then Malenkov dropped his hand and said, "I know. I am smudged." Could he really have known? Or was he guessing?

Answers on page 101.

Who Wants to Work for King Sadim?

Every month each of the six provinces of the Kingdom of Kardonia paid, as tribute to King Sadim, a quantity of gold proportional to its population. The payments were made in sacks of 16-ounce (448 g) nuggets.

One month the minister of finance reported to Sadim that one province was paying with nuggets that weighed only 15 ounces (420 g).

In a fury, Sadim told his minister: "Tomorrow morning, you shall place no more than 16 of the nuggets from the various sacks on the royal scale. If you cannot identify the guilty province when you learn the weight of these nuggets, you will be executed on the spot!"

How can the minister save his life?

Answer on page 101.

ANSWERS

PUZZLES

The Garbles

Toots is a Garble.
Nellie is not a Garble.
Stacy is a Garble.
Duke is not a Garble.
All Garbles have a circle as part of their equipment.

Your Hidden Hosts

One of the owners is at the top in the drapes. The other is in the leaves of the potted palm.

The Bermuda Rectangle

The Farfels

Sandy is a Farfel.
Liz is a Farfel.
Sasha is a Farfel.
Pierre is not a Farfel.
All Farfels have hair.

The Crown of Zown

The Traffic Accident

If your score is:
15–20: You're an excellent witness.
12–14: You're a better witness than most people.
Less: Not really awake, are you?

The Krippies

June is a Krippie.
Watch is not a Krippie.
Pansy is a Krippie.
Dragonfly is not a Krippie.
All Krippies are girls' names.

What's Missing?

1. mouth
2. eye
3. nose
4. spoon in right hand
5. chimney through roof (no credit for smoke)
6. ear
7. filament wires
8. stamp
9. strings
10. rivet at other end of knife

8–10 right: Excellent
6– 7 right: Good
4– 5 right: Fair
Less: Poor

Egg Fu Yong Vanishes

Observation Test

Score one point for each correct item. Deduct one point for any item you wrote down that is not actually in the scene. The picture contains 33 items:

ashtray	flowers
barometer	girl
birdcage	guitar
book	kitten
boy	lamp
candlestick	mantel
chairs	mirror
clock	picture
curtains	rug
cushion	shade
dish	table, large
dog	table, small
doll	television set
door	tricycle
drapes	vase
electric outlet	window
fireplace	

89

25 or more: Excellent
21–24: Good
18–20 Fair
Less: Poor

The Paraglops
Ralphie is a Paraglop.
Rapunzel is a Paraglop.
Leonard is not a Paraglop.
Hazel is a Paraglop.
All Paraglops wear some kind of decoration.

The Nifties
The Oaks is not a Niftie.
Leffanoe's Castle is a Niftie.
Charlie's Garage is not a Niftie.
The Church is not a Niftie.
All Nifties have 5 rectangular windows.

What's Missing This Time?
1. trigger
2. tail
3. leg on left side (not a claw)
4. one cat's shadow
5. a bowling ball for the man, placed in his hand
6. net
7. left arm
8. controls on television set
9. hand and powder puff in mirror
10. diamond in upper left of card

8–10 right: Excellent
6–7 right: Good
4–5 right: Fair
Less: Poor

The Ribbles
Hepzibah is not a Ribble.
Igor is a Ribble.
The Baron is a Ribble.
Mrs. Hyde is not a Ribble.
All Ribbles keep their mouths shut.

TESTS
Test Your Memory for Words
To find your score, deduct two points for each word you omitted. For each word that you had in the wrong order, deduct one point.

54 or better: Excellent
48–54: Good
40–48: Fair
Less: You can improve your memory with practice. Try this test again!

Test Your Memory for Shapes
To get your score, count your mistakes:

0–1 mistake: Excellent memory for shapes
2–3: Good
4: Fair
5 or more: Poor. Try the test again.

Are You a Good Organizer?

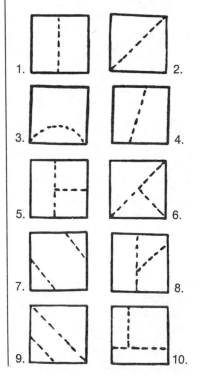

90

8 to 10 correct: Excellent
6 or 7 correct: Good
5 correct: Fair
Less: Poor

Are You Thorough?

1. 1 and 16
2. 5 and 7 and 18
3. 9
4. 3 and 19
5. 2 and 20
6. 8
7. 10

For each *exactly* correct answer allow yourself a credit of 2 points.

12 or more credits: Excellent
10 or 11 credits: Good
9 credits: Fair
Less: You worked either too quickly or too carelessly.

Are You Accurate?

The following pairs are identical:
1, 3, 4, 6, 10, 11, 13, 16, 17, 18, 20, 24, 25.
For unfinished numbers count 1/2. For errors count 1 point.

Debit of 0 to 3: Excellent
Debit of 4 to 6: Good
Debit of 7 or 8: Fair
Debit over 8: Too careless

Test Your Concentration: Concentrating on Numbers

There were 24 pairs of numbers to be circled:

(a)	(9 1) (2 8) (3 7)		Total 3
(b)	(6 4) (8 2)		2
(c)	(3 7) (2 8)		2
(d)	(5 5) (2 8) (7 3)	(9 1)	4
(e)	(2 8) (3 7)		2
(f)	(3 7)		1
(g)	(3 7) (8 2) (4 6)	(5 5)	4
(h)	(8 2) (3 7) (4 6)		3
(i)	(5 5) (9 1)		2
(j)	(1 9)		1

20 or more: Excellent
18 or 19: Good
16 or 17: Fair
Less: Poor concentration

Concentrating on Letters

1. IF YOU
2. DO WELL THE
3. MINOR TASKS
4. WHICH YOU
5. ARE CALLED
6. UPON
7. TO PERFORM YOU
8. WILL HAVE BUT LITTLE
9. DIFFICULTY WITH
10. THE BIGGER ONES

20 or more: Excellent
18 or 19: Good
16 or 17: Fair
Less: Try harder to disregard extraneous disturbances.

Are You Precise?

```
1 5 4 2 7 6 3 5 7 2 8 5 4 6 3 7 2 8 1
- ∪ ∟ ⋀ ∧ ⊙ ⊐ ∪⋀ ⋈ ✕ ∪ ∟⊙ ⊐⋀⋈ ✕ -
        9 5 8 4 7 3
        = ∪ ✕ ∟ ⋀ ⊐
6 2 5 1 9 2 8 3 7 4 6 5 9 4 8 3 7 2 6
⊙ ⋈ ∪- = ⋈ ✕ ⊐⋀ ∟ ⊙ ∪ = ∟ ✕ ⊐⋀⋀⊙
        1 5 4 6 3 7
        - ∪ ∟ ⊙ ⊐⋀
```

45 to 50: Excellent
40 to 45: Good
35 to 40: Satisfactory
Less: You need to concentrate more when you do detail work.

Are You Efficient?

```
3 1 2 1 3 2 1 4 2 3 5 2 9 1 4
⊐ - ⋈ - ⊐ ⋈ - ∟ ⋈ ⊐ ∪ ⋈ = - ∟

6 3 1 5 4 2 7 6 3 8 7 2 9 5 4
⊙ ⊐ - ∪ ∟ ⋀ ⋀ ⊙ ⊐ ✕ ⋀ ⋈ = ∪ ∟

6 3 7 2 8 1 9 5 8 4 7 3 6 9 5
⊙ ⊐ ⋀ ⋈ ✕ - = ∪ ✕ ∟ ⋀ ⊐ ⊙ = ∪
```

Score yourself on the number of seconds it took you, but add 2 seconds for each incorrect symbol.

Under 90 seconds: Excellent
90 to 100 seconds: Good
100 to 120 seconds: Fair
120 or more: You need
                    to concen-
                    trate more
                    on detail
                    work.

How Is Your Manual Dexterity?

Count 1 point for each tap correctly made. Deduct 2 points for
each error. Count each of these as
errors:

  a box you skipped
  two dots in same box
  dot striking a line

96 or more: Excellent
86 to 96:   Good
80 to 84:   Fair
Less: Poor

Test Your Sense of Spatial Relationships

(a) 27   (e) 19   (i) 13
(b) 15   (f) 40   (j) 20
(c) 15   (g) 10   (k) 50
(d) 18   (h) 22

10 or 11 correct: Excellent
8 or 9 correct: Good
7 correct: Fair
Less: Poor

Copyreading Aptitude Test

The following lines contain errors:
1 2 4 6 7 9 10 11 13 14

More than 3 errors means that you
are a careless copyreader. You can
overcome this with practice.

Personality Tests: In a Dream Garden

1. Your description of your ideal
   garden is a description of the
   way you want everyone to think
   of you.

2 & 3. Your description of the
house and where it is in relation
to the garden is a description of
the way you see yourself in relation to the rest of the world.

4. Your description of the key is a
   description of your friend-
   ships—how simple or compli-
   cated they are.

5. What you do when you lose your
   key tells what you do when
   something goes wrong in a
   friendship.

6. Whatever you choose to describe
   represents the artistic side of
   your nature, your imagination.

7. The action you take reveals
   what you do when you are faced
   with an obstacle.

Walking in the Woods

Question #1 is a test of your attitude towards other people.

If you answered (a), you are outgoing and friendly and sometimes,
perhaps, not as cautious as you
might be.

If you answered (b), you wait for
other people to approach you, of-
fering your friendship only to a
few.

If you answered (c), your attitude
towards others is based on common sense.

Question #2 is a test of your attitude towards your friends.

If you answered (a), your friend-
ships are often casual and even
when you are very friendly, you
make few demands on rela-
tionships.

If you answered (b), you are
easily offended and don't open up
easily even to your closest friends.

If you answered (c), you are pos-
sessive of your friends, demanding
and quite jealous.

Question #3 is a test of your attitude towards experiences.

If you answered (a), you test out new activities before you commit yourself to them.

If you answered (b), you rush into new things and often drop them.

If you answered (c), you are reluctant to participate in new activities and hold yourself aloof from things that might really interest you if you gave them a chance.

Question #4 is a test of your attitude towards life. If you answered (a), you run away from it.

If you answered (b), you wait to see what is going to happen before taking action.

If you answered (c), you go out to meet if, often without thinking!

Are You an Extrovert or an Introvert?

Give yourself 1 point for every "Yes" answer. Then deduct 2 points off for any of the following questions which you answered "Yes": (1) (6) (7) (10) (13) (20) (26) (27) (28) (29) (31) (35) (37) (38) (39).

If you scored:

Between 16 and 25: You answered the questions as an extrovert.

Between 6 and 15: Your answers fell in between the two.

Below 6: You answered the questions as an introvert.

WORD GAMES
Word Hunt

AMELIORATE

alarm	marital	remit
alate	marl	remote
alit	mart	retail
altar	martial	rialto
alter	mate	riata
alto	matelote	rile
aorta	mater	rime
area	material	riot
areate	meal	rite
areole	meat	roam
aria	melt	roil
aril	mere	role
aroma	merit	rote
atelier	metal	tail
earl	meteor	tailor
elate	meter	tale
elite	mile	tame
emir	mire	tare
emit	mite	taro
emote	mitre	teal
eral	moat	team
irate	mole	tear
item	molt	teem
iter	moral	term
lair	morale	tiara
lama	more	tile
lame	mortal	time
lariat	mote	timer
late	motel	tire
later	omelet	toil
leer	omit	toile
lerot	oral	tole
liar	orale	tome
lime	orate	tore
lira	rail	trail
liter	rate	trailer
loam	ratel	tram
loiter	ratio	tremor
lore	real	trial
mail	realm	trim
male	ream	trio
malt	reel	
mare	relate	

CONSTRUCTION

coin	occur	strict
conic	onion	strut
consort	onto	stun
constrict	onus	stunt
construct	oust	succor
contort	roon	suction
contour	roost	suit
confusion	root	tint
coon	rout	tocsin
coot	ruction	tonic
corn	ruin	toot
cost	runt	torn
cotton	rust	torso
count	rustic	tort
court	scion	tour
cousin	scoot	tout
croon	scorn	trot
crouton	scour	trout
crust	scout	trust
curio	snort	tunic
curt	snout	turn
icon	soon	unction
incur	soot	unicorn
instruct	sour	union
into	sort	unison
iron	stint	unit
noon	stir	unto
notion	stoic	
noun	stout	

DEVELOPING

deep	dove	glove
deign	dung	golden
dele	edge	gone
delve	elide	idle
depone	elope	idol
devein	endive	ingle
develop	envelop	ledge
devil	envied	legend
dine	even	lend
ding	evil	levied
dinge	geode	lied
dive	gild	liege
doge	give	lien
doing	glee	ling
dole	glen	lion
dope	glide	live

liven	olden	pole
lodge	olive	pond
loge	open	pone
loin	opine	veil
long	oven	vein
lope	ovine	vend
love	pend	vile
need	pied	vine
node	pile	viol
novel	pine	void
ogee	plied	voile
ogle	plod	

ESTABLISH

abet	blithe	sale
able	east	salt
aisle	habit	sash
alit	hail	sate
assist	hale	seal
bail	halt	seat
bait	hassle	shale
bale	hast	shalt
base	haste	shies
bash	hate	silt
basil	heal	sisal
basis	heat	slab
bass	heist	slash
basset	hilt	slat
bast	hiss	slate
baste	isle	slit
bath	istle	stab
bathe	lash	stable
beast	lass	stale
beat	last	stash
belt	late	steal
best	lath	sties
bias	lathe	stile
bile	leash	table
bite	least	tail
blase	less	tale
blast	lest	tassel
bleat	list	teal
bless	sable	this
blest	sahib	tile
bliss	sail	

IRREGULARLY

ague	gruel	real
airy	guile	really
alley	gull	rear
ally	gully	regal
argue	gyre	regular
argyle	lager	relay
aril	lair	rely
earl	large	rile
early	largely	rill
gale	layer	rule
gall	leary	ruler
galley	legal	ruly
gayer	liar	rural
gear	lira	ugly
girl	lure	urge
glare	lyre	year
glue	rage	yell
grail	rail	yule
gray	rally	
grey	rare	
grill	rarely	

PRECIOUS

cope	peri	score
copse	pier	scour
core	pious	scrip
corpse	pore	sire
coup	poser	sirup
coupe	pour	sore
course	precis	soup
crisp	price	sour
crop	prose	spice
croupe	puce	spire
cruise	pure	spore
cure	purse	spruce
curse	recoup	spur
cusp	rice	suer
ecru	rise	super
epic	rope	sure
icer	rose	user
osier	ruse	
ours	scope	

See page 102 for Categories word lists.

See page 102 for Categories word lists.

QUIZZES

Literature Quiz

Two-Point Questions
1. *Kidnapped.*
2. Jules Verne.
3. *Don Quixote.*
4. "The Ides of March" (March 15).

Three-Point Questions
1. *Utopia.*
2. *Pilgrim's Progress*, an allegory based on the adventures of Christian on his way from the City of Destruction to the Celestial City.
3. King Arthur.
4. Eugene O'Neill.

Five-Point Questions
1. Mrs. Malaprop.
2. *Robinson Crusoe* by Daniel Defoe.
3. *The House of the Seven Gables.*
4. *Ulysses* by James Joyce.

Bad Guys Quiz
Two-Point Questions
1. Nero.
2. Sitting Bull.
3. Scrooge.
4. Attila.

Three-Point Questions
1. Iago.
2. Jean Lafitte.
3. Fagin.
4. The Devil.

Five- Point Questions
1. Javert.
2. General Zaroff.
3. Niccolo Machiavelli.
4. The Duke of Alva.

Mythology Quiz
Two-Point Questions
1. Cupid.
2. The Golden Fleece.
3. Hercules.
4. Olympus, a mountain in Macedonia.

Three-Point Questions
1. Cyclopes (plural for Cyclops).
2. Alexander the Great.
3. Narcissus.
4. Janus, the god of doorways and entrances (January was named after him).

Five-Point Questions
1. The winged horse, Pegasus.
2. Caduceus, a winged staff entwined by two serpents.
3. Charon.
4. The father was Daedalus, the son Icarus. Icarus' wings melted when he flew too near the sun.

Legends, Tales and Fables Quiz
Two Point Questions
1. Friar Tuck.
2. The Blarney Stone.
3. Sinbad the Sailor.
4. Huckleberry Finn.

Three-Point Questions
1. Athos, Porthos and Aramis.
2. The Jabberwock.
3. The phoenix.
4. Jim Hawkins.

Five-Point Questions
1. Jack and Jill.
2. Pygmalion.
3. Napoleon.
4. Modred

Famous People Quiz
Two-Point Questions
1. Florence Nightingale.
2. Walt Whitman.
3. Sir Isaac Newton.
4. Mary Pickford.

Three-Point Questions
1. Socrates.
2. King John.
3. Benvenuto Cellini.
4. Vasco da Gama.

Five-Point Questions
1. Wilhelm Röentgen.
2. Titian.
3. Friedrich Engels.
4. Jean and Auguste Piccard.

Bible Quiz
Two-Point Questions
1. Goliath.
2. John the Baptist.
3. Jerusalem.
4. Jonah.

Three-Point Questions
1. Sea of Galilee.
2. Abraham (or Abram).
3. Saul of Tarsus.
4. At Jericho, the defending walls tumbled when the trumpets blew.

Five-Point Questions
1. Ham, Shem and Japheth.
2. Jacob first married the older daughter, Leah, and later married Rachel.
3. Procurator of Judea.
4. 969 years.

Interesting Places Quiz
Two-Point Questions
1. Africa.
2. Australia.
3. Europe.
4. The Alps.
Three-Point Questions
1. North.
2. The Himalayas.
3. An ocean area (no land).
4. Caribbean.
Five-Point Questions
1. The Bund.
2. U.S. 66.
3. The Appian Way.
4. Easter Island.

Structures—Where Are They?
Two-Point Questions
1. Greece (Athens).

2. Egypt (Giza).
3. Italy (Rome).
4. England (London).

Three-Point Questions
1. India (Agra).
2. Italy (Rome); also France (Paris).
3. Spain (Granada).
4. Italy (Venice).

Five-Point Questions
1. Turkey (Istanbul).
2. Italy (Florence).
3. Spain (Madrid).
4. Israel (Jerusalem).

Rivers—Where Are They?
Two-Point Questions
1. China.
2. Alaska.
3. Austria-Hungary (boundary); also Germany (where it rises).
4. United States-Mexico (boundary).

Three-Point Questions
1. India.
2. U.S.S.R.
3. Canada.
4. Germany.

Five-Point Questions
1. Vietnam, Cambodia and Laos.
2. U.S.S.R.
3. Australia.
4. Brazil.

Volcanoes—Where Are They?
Two-Point Questions
1. Italy.
2. Japan.
3. Hawaii.
4. Mexico.

Three-Point Questions
1. United States (California).
2. Mexico.
3. Sicily.
4. Africa.

Five-Point Questions
1. Japan.

2. Sumatra.
3. Alaska.
4. Mexico.

Nursery Rhymes Quiz
Two-Point Questions
1. Tea.
2. Nine days old.
3. A plum.
4. Under the haystack (fast asleep).

Three-Point Questions
1. His master, his dame and the little boy who lived down the lane.
2. Some broth, without any bread.
3. Tuesday's child is full of grace.
4. A whale.

Five-Point Questions
1. "Over the Hills and Far Away."
2. Silver buckles.
3. "Are the children in bed? for it's now eight o'clock."
4. A very fine gander.

Who Are They in the Movies?
Two-Point Questions
1. Marilyn Monroe
2. Cary Grant
3. John Wayne
4. Judy Garland

Three-Point Questions
1. Ginger Rogers and Fred Astaire
2. Jack Benny and Fred Allen
3. Jerry Lewis and Dean Martin
4. Boris Karloff and Peter Lorre

Five-Point Questions
1. They are all comedians: Danny Kaye, George Burns, Milton Berle, Mel Brooks, W. C. Fields
2. They all specialized in glamor: Jean Harlow, Marlene Dietrich, Rita Hayworth, Brigitte Bardot, Sophia Loren
3. They all sing: Doris Day, Lotte Lenya, Vic Damone, Nat King Cole, Perry Como
4. They are all famous directors:

John Ford, D. W. Griffith, Mike Nichols, Michael Curtiz, Woody Allen

BRAINTEASERS
The Pufferbill in the Pear Tree

Not until the last day. Since the pufferbill ate twice as many leaves every day, on the 30th day, it ate twice as many as on the 29th.

New Year's Resolution

You would have saved 1,073,741,824 pennies (or $10,737,418.24)!

Cross-Country Tour

It looks as if you'll need a whole new set of four tires, doesn't it? But there's no reason to waste all that trunk space. Actually, you need only two spares. After 4,000 (6,400 km) miles you can remove the front tires and put on the two new spares. Then after 8,000 (12,800 km) miles, you remove the rear tires and replace them with the two taken off the front, and continue for the remaining 4,000 miles. But don't make any side trips!

Death Meets the Squire

If the squire died without waking, no one could possibly know what he had been dreaming.

Magic Fifteen

2	9	4
7	5	3
6	1	8

Send More Money

The letter M, because of its position in the bottom line, can only be a 1.

M also appears in the second line. That means that the letter S must be a large one, so that you have the 1 to carry over. S must be either 8 or 9; no other number would be large enough to work.

If S is 8 or 9, the letter O must be a 0; no other number would be small enough to work.

Looking at the next column, where O appears again, you know that 1 must be carried over—otherwise, E plus O would equal E. You can write this as E + 1 = N.

Looking at the next column, where N appears again, you can construct an equation:

N plus R—plus 1 (assuming* that a 1 is carried over)—equals E plus 10 (plus 10 because you know that 1 is carried over into the next column). So the equation becomes:

$$N + R + 1 = E + 10$$
$$N + R + 1 = N - 1 + 10$$
$$N + R = N - 2 + 10$$
$$N + R = N + 8$$
$$R = 8$$

*You are making only one assumption: that D and E in the first column add up to 10 or more, so that a 1 carries over into the next column. Assuming you are right, R is 8 (it is 9 if your assumption is wrong).

So, going along with this assumption, you know that D and E can't add up to 10 exactly because you have used up the 0. You know they can't add up to 11, because you've used up the 1. You have also used up the 8(R) and the 9(S). What is left?

D and E could be 7 and 6. They

98

could be 7 and 5. But no other combinations are possible.

One of them is definitely 7. Can it be E? No, because then N would have to be 8, and you have already used up 8. Therefore D must be 7.

E must be 5. If E was 6, N would have to be 7, which is impossible because D is 7.

Y becomes 2, N becomes 6, and the sum works:

$$9\,5\,6\,7$$
$$\underline{1\,0\,8\,5}$$
$$1\,0\,6\,5\,2$$

Famous 45

8, 12, 5, 20. The result in each case is 10.

Dividing the Loaves

The judge was correct. There were 8 loaves in all, and to divide them equally, each loaf was cut into thirds, giving a total of 24 parts. Each man then ate 8 parts, and the stranger paid with 8 coins of equal value. The Arab who had had 5 loaves (15 parts) consumed 8 himself and the other 7 went to the stranger. The Arab with 3 loaves (9 parts) ate 8 himself and so he contributed only 1 to the stranger. Accordingly, the coins should be divided 7 and 1, as the judge proclaimed.

Dividing the Camels

Since 17 is a quantity which you cannot divide into halves, thirds, or ninths, and 18 is divisible by 2, 3 and 9, the Pharaoh's solution was to lend the brothers one camel. Then the eldest son received 9, the second son 6, and the third 2. Since this added up to only 17 anyway, the Pharaoh immediately took back the camel he had lent them. (It happens that the father had made provision for only 17/18 of his estate—1/2 plus 1/3 plus 1/9 equals 17/18!)

Who Is the Avon Lady?

From (3) you know that Jill is the model. Therefore she cannot be the Avon lady (2) or the actress (5). You also know she cannot be the sculptor or the race car driver (1). Therefore she must be the private detective; it is the only possibility left.

You know that Tracy is not the race car driver (6). Therefore, she must be the sculptor, since the sculptor and the race car driver are different people (1). Since Tracy is the sculptor, she cannot be the actress, since the two are roommates (4).

Therefore, Liz is the actress and the race car driver, and Tracy must be the Avon lady.

What Is the Name of the Largest Rabbit in the World?

If Jim's leg has been in a cast for 2 months (2) he cannot be the owner of the baboon(3) or the rabbit (1) who just played soccer with his owner yesterday. Therefore, Jim is the owner of the penguin, whose name is Jarvis.

Since the baboon bit Marvin (4), the baboon must be Spot—and therefore Marvin is the largest rabbit in the world.

African Thinking Game

Every member of the Elephant tribe always tells the truth. Agassu, who says he is *not* an Elephant, cannot be an Elephant, whether he is telling the truth or lying.

Since every member of the Leopard tribe always lies, Agassu, who says he is not an Elephant, cannot be a Leopard. Agassu must therefore be a Crocodile.

We know that Coffi cannot be a Crocodile, because Agassu is a

Crocodile. Therefore Coffi, who says he is not a Crocodile, is telling the truth. He cannot be a lying Leopard. He must be a truthful Elephant. And Diamala must be an Elephant, too, because truthful Coffi says so.

The Mailbox Mystery
The vice-president *mailed* the mailbox key, so the envelope containing it was deposited in the locked mailbox. It certainly was not the housekeeper's fault.

The Two Brothers
The brother simply said, "Let's swap horses!" The king's will stated that the son whose *horse* arrived second would get the fortune. Therefore, by riding the other one's horse, the winner of the race could be sure his own horse would be second at the castle gate. So they swapped and sped off.

Cannibals and Missionaries
In order not to have the cannibals outnumber the missionaries at any time, first the king rowed one cannibal across and then returned for a second cannibal. The cannibal king returned and two missionaries took the boat. One missionary returned, bringing a cannibal with him. All safe so far. Now a missionary went across with the king and brought back a cannibal. Then the two missionaries rowed across, and the cannibal king took the boat. He went back for the other two cannibals, whom he ferried across in two round trips. Altogether, 13 tries were required.

The Wise King
The king provided that one son was to divide the possessions, while the other son was to have first choice!

The Casket and the Basket
The king began correctly. When the prince got into the basket, he caused the basket with the casket to rise. The casket was taken out, and the queen got into the basket, causing the prince to rise as she descended. Then both the queen and prince stepped out, and the casket was lowered again. The queen got in with the casket (110 plus 80 pounds [55 + 40 kg]) and rose as the king descended. The king stayed on the ground; the queen stepped out and lowered the casket again. The prince went down, bringing up the casket once more. The queen removed the casket, got into the basket herself and descended, bringing up the prince. Both queen and prince stepped out. Then the prince lowered the casket, stepped into the other basket and descended, bringing up the casket to the empty tower. When the prince stepped out, the basket with the casket fell to the ground, and the royal family escaped with all its jewels!

Madness at the Bike Shop
Since each vehicle has two pedals, there are altogether 136 ÷ 2 or 68 vehicles. If X is the number of bicycles and Y is the number of tricycles, then:

$$X + Y = 68$$

Since each bicycle has two wheels and each tricycle has three wheels, the total number of wheels must be

$$2X + 3Y$$

But this number equals 153.

We know that 2X and 2Y equals 2 × 68, or 136. Therefore, the 3rd Y must be 153 − 136, or 17. And X is 51.

There are 51 bicycles and 17 tricycles.

The Tennis Nut

This problem contains extraneous information. Rodney has played 46 matches since July 1st, 26 of them on weekdays. Therefore, 20 weekend matches have been played. On the weekends two matches a day were played; so a total of ten weekend days has elapsed. In all, 26 + 10 = 36 days which have elapsed since July 1st. So yesterday was August 5th, today is the 6th, and when Rodney sees his boss today he's going to get the axe. He has no time at all.

The Mutilated Dictionary

Each page has 25 entries, 11 of which have been mutilated. This leaves 14 entries intact and lying between the first five and last six entries on each page.

In every group of 14 entries there are exactly two illustrations, for three illustrations occupy at least 15 entries, while one illustration occupies at most 13 entries.

Since there are two illustrations remaining on each of the book's 632 pages, there must be 2 × 632 or 1,264 illustrations left.

Revolution in Platonia

The king was imprisoned; the prime minister was executed; the treasurer was freed.

Since all three men received different sentences, the king was not executed and the prime minister was not imprisoned.

The treasurer was freed because the other two men received different sentences.

Thus the king could not have been executed or freed, so he was imprisoned.

The prime minister must have received the remaining sentence and was therefore executed.

Russian Tunnel

Malenkov was *not* guessing. He reasoned this way: "I know the other two are smudged because I can see them. Either I am smudged or I am not smudged. If I am not smudged, then Molotov and Vishinsky raised their hands because each saw the other was smudged. So, if I am not smudged, each of the other two would know that he himself was smudged, and each would be able to drop his hand. They haven't done this, so I *must* be smudged."

Because of this incident, it is said, Stalin chose Malenkov as his successor.

Who Wants to Work for King Sadim?

If the minister puts on the scale one nugget from the first province, two from the second, three from the third, four from the fourth, five from the fifth, and none from the sixth province, he can determine which province is guilty.

If the sixth province is guilty, the nuggets will weigh 240 ounces (6720 g), because each nugget on the scale will weigh 16 ounces (448 g).

If the fifth province is guilty, the scale will show 235 ounces (6580 g), for it will hold 10 16-ounce (448-g) nuggets and 5 15-ounce (420-g) nuggets. If the fourth province is guilty, the scale will show a weight of 236 ounces (6608 g), for it will hold 11 16-ounce (448-g) nuggets and 4 15-ounce (420-g) nuggets

And so on. So if the minister observes the weight given by the scale, he will be able to identify the guilty province immediately and save his life.

In any case, he'd be wise to look for a new job.

Aaron 2
Abbas 10
Abbotson 7
Abbott 3
Abel 1
Abiezer 10
Abijah 10
Abirah 10
Abishur 10
Abner 3
Abric 10
Abros 10
Absalom 4
Ace 1
Achilles 5
Achsel 10
Ackerley 10
Adair 6
Adal 10
Adalric 10
Adam 1
Adamson 8
Adar 10
Addis 10
Addison 3
Addo 10
Adel 10
Adelbert 8
Adelgar 10
Adelhart 10
Adelmo 10
Adelwin 10
Adlai 4
Adlar 10
Adlo 10
Admetus 8
Adolf 2
Adolph 1
Adolphus 4
Adon 10
Adonis 4
Adrian 4
Adriel 10
Aeneas 7
Agar 9

Ahrens 7
Aidan 10
Aiken 10
Ainsley 8
Ainsworth 8
Airell 10
Airlie 10
Ajax 5
Alain 5
Alair 7
Alan 1
Aland 10
Alanson 9
Alanus 10
Alard 10
Alaric 8
Alastair 4
Alayne 8
Alban 7
Alber 10
Alberic 10
Albern 10
Albert 1
Albin 6
Albion 8
Albright 8
Alcides 10
Alcott 8
Alda 10
Alden 3
Alder 10
Alderley 10
Aldith 10
Aldo 4
Aldous 4
Aldred 10
Aldric 10
Aldrich 10
Aldwin 10
Alec 1
Aleron 10
Alexander 1
Alexis 3
Aleyn 4
Alf 7

Alford 10
Alfred 1
Algar 8
Alger 9
Algernon 5
Alison 4
Allain 9
Allan 1
Allard 9
Allen 1
Alleyn 3
Allison 7
Allister 10
Almaric 10
Alois 10
Alonzo 4
Aloysius 3
Alpheus 10
Alphonso 3
Alred 10
Alric 8
Alroy 10
Alston 8
Altair 10
Alton 9
Alvan 10
Alver 10
Alvernon 10
Alvin 1
Alvis 5
Alvord 10
Alwin 3
Alworth 10
Alwyn 4
Amadeus 8
Amadis 10
Amaldo 10
Amalric 10
Amasa 10
Ambert 10
Ambler 10
Ambrose 4
Amery 6
Amiel 10
Amin 10

Amon 10
Amory 3
Amos 1
Amparo 10
Amsden 10
Anastasius 7
Anatole 6
Ancel 5
Anders 10
Anderson 6
Andre 3
Andrew 1
Andros 10
Angel 7
Angelo 2
Angus 4
Anis 10
Annibal 10
Anoki 10
Ansel 6
Anselm 8
Anson 8
Anthony 1
Antol 10
Anton 6
Antoniades 7
Antonio 3
Antony 1
Apollo 7
Ara 10
Arad 10
Arber 10
Archer 8
Archibald 4
Ardel 10
Arden 10
Ardeth 10
Ardmore 8
Ardolph 10
Arend 10
Argyle 10
Ari 8
Arian 10
Aric 10
Ariel 7

Aristides 10
Aristo 10
Aristocles 10
Aristotle 10
Arius 10
Arkwright 10
Arlen 5
Arles 7
Arlet 10
Arleth 10
Arley 9
Arlin 7
Arlo 6
Arlyn 10
Armand 6
Armando 5
Armen 10
Armstrong 10
Arnold 1
Aron 10
Arrigo 10
Arsen 8
Artemid 10
Artemus 10
Arthur 1
Arturo 3
Arundel 9
Arvel 10
Arvin 10
Asa 6
Ashbrook 10
Ashburne 10
Ashby 8
Ashcroft 10
Asher 10
Ashford 10
Ashley 4
Athel 10
Athelstan 10
Athmore 10
Attwood 8
Atwater 10
Atwell 10
Atwood 10
Aubert 10

Aubin 10
Aubrey 3
Audley 10
Audrey 4
Audric 10
Audwin 10
August 6
Augustine 8
Augustus 7
Aurelio 8
Aurelius 8
Aurick 10
Austin 3
Avalon 10
Averil 8
Avery 5
Avin 10
Axel 4
Aylett 10
Aylmar 8
Aylsworth 10
Aylward 10
Aylwin 10
Aymon 10
Azar 10
Azel 10

Bailey 10
Bainbridge 8
Baird 10
Baldric 10
Baldur 10
Baldwin 7
Balfour 8
Ballard 8
Bancroft 7
Banning 9
Bannister 7
Barbour 10
Barclay 4
Bardo 10
Barker 7
Barkham 6
Barlow 5
Barnabas 4

Barnaby 3
Barnard 8
Barnett 6
Barney 3
Barnum 8
Barrett 7
Barron 8
Barry 1
Barstow 7
Bart 6
Barthold 10
Bartholomew 2
Bartlett 8
Bartolo 10
Barton 7
Bartram 10
Basil 3
Bassett 10
Bateman 9
Baxter 8
Bayard 10
Bayley 10
Bayliss 10
Baylor 10
Beau 5
Beauford 10
Beaufort 10
Beaumont 10
Beauregard 10
Bela 6
Belcher 10
Belden 10
Bellamy 8
Belmont 8
Ben 1
Benedict 3
Benito 5
Benjamin 1
Bennett 6
Benno 10
Bentley 6
Benton 8
Benvenuto 5
Beppo 7
Beresford 8

Berg 10
Berger 5
Berkeley 8
Berman 8
Bernaldo 6
Bernard 1
Bernardo 2
Bernhard 3
Bernold 10
Bert 2
Berton 5
Bertram 1
Bertrand 10
Bertwin 10
Berward 10
Berwick 10
Berwin 10
Bevan 8
Beverley 3
Bevis 10
Bill 1
Billy 1
Blaine 6
Blair 8
Blake 8
Blakeman 10
Blanchard 5
Blanco 10
Blandon 8
Bliss 8
Boaz 3
Bob 1
Boden 10
Bolton 8
Boniface 8
Bonner 10
Booth 7
Borden 7
Boris 2
Bostwick 10
Boswell 6
Bothwell 8
Bourke 6
Bourne 10
Bowden 10

Bowen 4	Burbank 6	Carroll 5	Clayborne 10
Bowie 8	Burden 7	Carter 6	Clayton 4
Boyce 9	Burgess 2	Cartwright 8	Clem 1
Boyd 7	Burke 3	Carvel 9	Clemence 4
Boyle 7	Burley 8	Carver 6	Clement 3
Boynton 8	Burnell 7	Cary 5	Cleon 10
Bradburn 9	Burnett 5	Caryl 8	Cleve 10
Bradbury 7	Burney 6	Casey 3	Cliff 3
Braden 9	Burton 2	Casimir 5	Clifford 2
Bradfield 8	Byram 4	Caspar 3	Clifton 4
Bradford 6	Bryan 4	Cass 4	Clinton 5
Bradley 5	Byrne 5	Cassidy 8	Clive 4
Bradshaw 8	Byron 7	Cassius 6	Clovis 6
Brady 6		Castor 8	Clyde 2
Brainard 10	Cadell 10	Caswell 8	Clymer 9
Brand 10	Cadman 10	Cato 7	Colbert 6
Brandon 5	Cadmar 10	Cavanagh 6	Colburn 8
Brant 6	Cadmus 10	Cavendish 8	Colby 3
Brendan 5	Cadoc 10	Cecil 3	Cole 4
Brent 7	Cadwallader 10	Cedric 4	Coleman 7
Brett 4	Caesar 2	Cesaro 5	Coley 5
Brewster 4	Cain 4	Chad 6	Colin 7
Brian 2	Calbert 6	Chancellor 8	Collier 8
Brice 8	Caldwell 5	Chandler 6	Collins 6
Brien 5	Caleb 6	Chapin 7	Compton 7
Brigham 4	Callahan 8	Chapman 9	Conan 6
Brion 6	Calvert 6	Charles 1	Conant 5
Brisbane 8	Calvin 5	Charlton 6	Condon 7
Bristow 9	Camden 7	Chauncey 4	Conger 8
Brisbane 8	Cameron 7	Chelsea 8	Connell 6
Britton 8	Campbell 4	Cheney 9	Connor 5
Brock 6	Canfield 7	Chesley 7	Conover 6
Broderick 3	Carew 10	Chester 2	Conrad 3
Brodie 7	Carey 6	Chet 2	Conroy 6
Bromfield 8	Carl 1	Chris 1	Constantine 7
Brooke 5	Carleton 3	Christian 4	Conway 5
Bruce 1	Carlisle 7	Christopher 1	Copeland 8
Bruno 5	Carlo 3	Cicero 6	Corbett 6
Brutus 7	Carlos 2	Clair 5	Corcoran 5
Bryan 4	Carlton 2	Clarence 1	Corey 6
Bryce 6	Carlyle 7	Clark 1	Cornelius 3
Bryon 8	Carmichael 4	Claude 3	Cornell 6
Buchanan 4	Carmody 10	Claudius 4	Corydon 10
Budd 5	Carney 10	Claus 6	Cosgrove 9
Buddy 5	Carol 6	Clay 8	Cosmo 3

Cotton 8
Courtland 7
Courtney 4
Cowan 6
Craig 1
Crandall 10
Crawford 4
Creon 5
Crispin 8
Cromwell 7
Culbert 5
Cullen 8
Culver 3
Curt 4
Curtis 4
Cuthbert 4
Cutler 5
Cyrano 5
Cyril 4
Cyrus 3

Dale 5
Dallas 9
Dalton 8
Daly 6
Damien 5
Damon 4
Dan 1
Dana 4
Dane 3
Danforth 9
Daniel 1
Darby 5
Darcy 4
Darian 5
Darius 6
Darnell 8
Darrell 4
Darwin 8
Daryl 3
David 1
Davis 5
Dawes 7
Dean 6
Delano 9

Delavan 7
Delbert 4
Delmar 8
Delwin 9
Demosthenes 8
Dempsey 6
Denham 9
Denis 3
Denison 5
Denman 9
Dennis 1
Denys 1
Derby 8
Derek 4
Dermot 4
Derrick 5
Derward 7
Derwin 9
Desmond 3
Devereaux 7
Devin 2
Devlin 4
Dewar 8
De Witt 7
Dexter 3
Dick 1
Digby 6
Dillard 4
Dillon 9
Dilwin 6
Dion 5
Dirk 7
Dixon 5
Dmitri 5
Domingo 7
Dominic 4
Don 1
Donaghan 5
Donahue 7
Donald 1
Donaldson 5
Donato 6
Donegal 5
Donnelly 6
Donovan 3

Doran 7
Dorian 4
Douglas 1
Doyle 4
Drew 5
Driscoll 3
Drummond 6
Drury 8
Dryden 6
Duane 4
Dudley 3
Duff 7
Duke 1
Dunbar 4
Duncan 3
Dunham 4
Dunlap 7
Dunstan 9
Durand 8
Durant 8
Durham 6
Durward 8
Durwin 10
Dustin 4
Dwayne 3
Dwight 3
Dyre 9

Earl 2
Eben 5
Ebenezer 4
Eberhart 8
Ebert 7
Ed 1
Edan 8
Edelbert 10
Edgar 3
Edmond 1
Edmund 1
Edsel 7
Edward 1
Edwardo 5
Edwin 2
Egan 5
Egbert 3

Egerton 9
Egmont 8
Ehrman 10
Elbert 4
Eldon 7
Eldred 10
Eldridge 10
Elgin 8
Eli 3
Elia 7
Elias 4
Eliezer 10
Elihu 9
Elijah 5
Eliot 3
Elisha 10
Ellery 2
Elliott 3
Ellis 6
Ellsworth 8
Elmer 1
Elmo 1
Elroy 2
Elton 10
Elvin 5
Elvis 4
Elwin 4
Elwood 6
Elwyn 4
Ely 2
Emeric 9
Emerson 4
Emery 3
Emil 2
Emlyn 8
Emmanuel 5
Emmet 6
Emory 3
Endicott 7
Engelbert 4
Ennis 8
Enoch 4
Enos 5
Enrico 4
Ensign 5

Ephriam 3	Ferdinand 3	Garrick 7	Gregory 1
Erasmus 7	Fergus 6	Garrison 8	Grenville 7
Erastus 8	Fernando 4	Garth 5	Gresham 9
Erbert 7	Ferrand 8	Garver 7	Griswold 3
Erhard 6	Ferris 9	Garvin 6	Grosvenor 6
Eric 1	Fidel 5	Garwood 8	Grover 5
Erland 7	Fielding 7	Gary 1	Guido 4
Erle 6	Findlay 8	Gaston 4	Guilford 7
Ernest 5	Fitzgerald 5	Gavin 5	Gunther 4
Errol 4	Fleming 9	Gawain 7	Gus 1
Erskine 7	Fletcher 3	Gaye 8	Gustave 3
Erwin 3	Florentz 6	Gayle 6	Guthrie 6
Esau 7	Florian 7	Gaylord 8	Guy 4
Esmond 9	Floris 8	Gene 1	Gwyn 9
Estevan 8	Floyd 4	Geoffrey 1	
Ethan 3	Follett 8	Geordie 3	Hadley 7
Ethelbert 7	Ford 6	George 1	Haines 8
Eugene 1	Forrest 5	Gerald 1	Hal 1
Eustace 3	Forrester 9	Gerard 1	Hale 5
Evan 4	Fortescue 10	Gerold 4	Hallam 10
Evar 10	Foster 4	Gideon 5	Halstead 10
Evel 6	Fowler 6	Gifford 4	Haman 8
Evelyn 7	Franchot 5	Gilbert 2	Hamilton 5
Everard 10	Francis 1	Giles 5	Hamlet 5
Everett 3	Frank 1	Gilford 8	Hamlyn 8
Evers 7	Franklin 1	Gillian 7	Hamnet 10
Evert 10	Fraser 5	Gilmore 7	Hamon 8
Ewan 7	Fred 1	Gilroy 9	Hank 1
Ewart 8	Frederic 1	Giovanni 3	Hanley 9
Ewell 6	Freeman 5	Girard 5	Hannibal 8
Ewing 8	Fremont 7	Gladwin 9	Hans 3
Ezekiel 4	Fritz 4	Glen 6	Hansel 4
Ezra 2		Goddard 7	Harald 4
	Gabriel 5	Godfrey 4	Harcourt 7
Fabian 7	Gaines 4	Godwin 7	Harding 5
Fairchild 7	Galahad 7	Gomer 6	Hardy 7
Fairfax 8	Gale 7	Goodwin 8	Hargrave 8
Farley 4	Galen 10	Gordon 1	Harlan 6
Farmer 9	Gallagher 9	Gouvenor 7	Harley 5
Farnham 7	Galvin 8	Graham 3	Harmon 8
Federico 5	Garcia 3	Grant 2	Harold 1
Fedor 6	Gardner 4	Grantham 8	Harper 4
Felipe 4	Garfield 8	Granville 7	Harris 5
Felix 3	Garland 10	Grayson 9	Harrison 6
Fenwick 9	Garret 9	Gregg 3	Harry 1

Hart 5
Harvey 1
Hastings 8
Havelock 6
Hayden 5
Hayes 8
Hayward 6
Heath 9
Hebert 10
Hector 4
Hedley 9
Heinrich 4
Henderson 8
Hendrik 3
Henley 7
Henri 3
Henry 1
Herald 9
Herbert 3
Hercules 7
Hereward 9
Herman 2
Hermes 7
Hernan 5
Herndon 7
Herod 8
Herschel 9
Hervey 8
Herwin 10
Heywood 6
Hezekiah 10
Hiawatha 10
Hieronymous 10
Hilary 8
Hilliard 10
Hillyer 10
Hiram 4
Hobart 8
Hoffman 7
Hogan 5
Holbrook 8
Holden 6
Hollis 4
Holman 6
Holmes 7

Homer 3
Honore 8
Horace 3
Horatio 4
Hortensio 9
Hosea 10
Howard 1
Howe 9
Howell 7
Howland 6
Hubbard 6
Hubert 3
Hugh 2
Hugo 4
Humphrey 4
Hunter 7
Huntley 9
Hutchins 5
Hyman 7

Iago 10
Ian 5
Ichabod 8
Ignace 8
Ignatius 10
Igor 5
Ike 2
Immanuel 9
Inglebert 9
Ingram 7
Innis 10
Ira 3
Irvin 7
Irving 3
Irwin 3
Isaac 2
Isadore 5
Isaiah 8
Ishmael 10
Israel 5
Ivan 5
Iver 10
Ivor 10

Jabez 10

Jack 1
Jackson 4
Jacob 1
Jacopo 9
Jacques 5
Jake 3
James 1
Jared 10
Jarrett 10
Jarvis 7
Jason 4
Jasper 7
Jay 5
Jed 4
Jedediah 10
Jefferson 6
Jeffrey 1
Jeremiah 6
Jeremy 4
Jerold 5
Jerome 4
Jerry 1
Jervis 6
Jess 3
Jesse 5
Jesus 6
Jethro 8
Jim 1
Job 10
Jocelin 8
Jock 6
Joe 1
Joel 5
John 1
Johnson 5
Jon 7
Jonah 5
Jonas 8
Jonathan 3
Jordan 6
Jose 1
Joseph 1
Joshua 4
Josiah 7
Joyce 8

Juan 1
Judah 9
Judd 3
Judson 8
Jules 6
Julian 3
Julius 4
Junior 8
Junius 9
Justin 5
Justus 10

Kane 10
Karl 1
Karsten 8
Keane 8
Kearney 8
Keating 7
Keenan 6
Keene 4
Keir 8
Keith 4
Keller 6
Kelly 5
Kelsey 10
Kelvin 8
Kelwin 10
Kendall 3
Kendrick 8
Kennedy 7
Kenneth 2
Kenrick 10
Kent 5
Kenton 7
Kenyon 4
Kermit 6
Kerry 4
Kerwin 5
Kevin 3
Kilburn 7
Kilroy 4
Kim 8
Kimball 9
Kingdon 8
Kingsley 10

Kingston 7
Kirby 5
Kirk 4
Kirkland 8
Kirkwood 5
Kit 6
Knight 10
Konrad 6
Kramer 8
Kurt 5
Kyle 5

Laird 4
Lambert 6
Lamont 7
Lance 7
Lancelot 4
Landis 7
Landon 8
Lane 8
Langdon 7
Langley 10
Langston 5
Larry 1
Lars 4
Latham 8
Lathrop 7
Latimer 9
Launcelot 7
Lauren 7
Laurence 1
Laurent 5
Lauritz 9
Lawlor 8
Lawrence 1
Lazarus 5
Leal 10
Leander 8
Lee 5
Lehman 5
Leigh 7
Leighton 8
Leith 7
Leland 7
Lemuel 8

Lennox 9
Leo 1
Leon 1
Leonard 1
Leonardo 3
Leonidas 8
Leopold 4
Leroy 2
Leslie 4
Lester 4
Lew 4
Lewis 2
Lincoln 7
Linden 8
Lindsay 8
Linn 9
Linus 7
Lionel 2
Lisle 5
Livingston 7
Llewellyn 6
Lloyd 4
Lochinvar 8
Lockwood 5
Logan 6
Lombard 8
Lon 3
Loren 8
Lorenz 4
Lorenzo 2
Lorillard 8
Lorimer 7
Lorin 5
Loring 7
Lorne 4
Lothario 6
Louis 1
Lovell 7
Lowell 6
Lucas 3
Lucian 5
Ludwig 4
Luis 3
Luke 3
Luther 6

Lyle 4
Lyman 8
Lyndon 5
Lynn 3
Lysander 9

Mac 2
Macauley 8
Mack 3
MacLeod 4
Maddox 7
Madison 8
Magan 7
Magellan 9
Magnus 7
Maitland 8
Malcolm 4
Mallory 5
Malone 7
Malvin 6
Mandel 8
Manfred 6
Manley 4
Manly 9
Manny 1
Mansfield 7
Manuel 5
Marc 1
Marcel 3
Marco 3
Marcus 7
Mario 3
Marion 5
Marius 8
Mark 1
Markham 6
Marlow 5
Marmaduke 7
Marmion 10
Marquand 8
Marsden 7
Marshall 3
Marston 8
Martin 1
Marvin 1

Mason 8
Mathias 7
Matthew 2
Maurice 2
Maury 4
Max 1
Maxim 8
Maximilian 7
Maxwell 5
Maynard 8
Mead 7
Medwin 7
Mel 2
Meldon 9
Melford 7
Melville 5
Melvin 1
Mercer 8
Meredith 7
Merivale 6
Merle 8
Merlin 9
Merrell 5
Merrick 7
Merritt 9
Merton 5
Mervin 4
Mervyn 6
Meryl 9
Meyer 7
Michael 1
Mickey 1
Miguel 3
Mike 1
Milbank 8
Milburn 7
Miles 3
Milford 5
Millard 7
Milo 4
Milton 2
Mitchell 5
Moe 3
Monroe 6
Montague 7

Monte 5
Montgomery 8
Moreland 6
Morell 8
Morgan 4
Morley 7
Morris 3
Mortimer 3
Morton 2
Moses 3
Munro 7
Murdock 5
Murphy 6
Murray 3
Murtagh 7
Myron 4

Napoleon 7
Narcissus 9
Nat 2
Nate 3
Nathan 2
Nathaniel 4
Neal 7
Ned 1
Needham 6
Nehemiah 7
Neil 5
Nemo 8
Neriah 10
Nero 7
Nestor 10
Neville 7
Nevin 6
Newcomb 6
Newell 7
Newlin 8
Newman 5
Newton 6
Nicholas 2
Nick 1
Nicodemus 7
Nigel 3
Nimrod 9
Noah 2

Noel 3
Nolan 9
Noland 7
Norbert 6
Norman 3
Norris 5
Norton 3
Norval 8
Norvin 8
Norwood 6
Nugent 7

Oakley 10
Obadiah 10
Octavius 6
Odell 8
Ogden 6
Olaf 7
Oleg 8
Olin 8
Oliver 3
Olney 6
Omar 4
Oral 8
Oran 10
Ordway 7
Oren 4
Orestes 9
Orin 6
Orion 7
Orlando 4
Orlin 7
Ormond 8
Orpheus 7
Orrin 5
Orsino 7
Orson 5
Orville 6
Osbert 7
Osborn 9
Oscar 2
Osgood 5
Osman 8
Osmond 7
Osric 8

Oswald 3
Othello 5
Otis 4
Otto 3
Owen 5

Pablo 5
Paddy 3
Page 8
Paige 4
Paine 8
Palmer 3
Pandro 8
Paolo 2
Parke 8
Parker 5
Parnell 4
Pascal 9
Pat 1
Patrice 5
Patrick 1
Paul 1
Paxton 9
Pedro 2
Pembroke 4
Pendleton 5
Penn 6
Percival 4
Percy 4
Pericles 7
Pernell 9
Perry 5
Peter 1
Phelan 8
Phil 1
Philander 10
Philbert 8
Philemon 9
Philip 1
Philo 5
Phineas 5
Pierce 6
Pierpont 5
Pierre 2
Pierson 8

Porter 7
Powell 7
Prentice 6
Prescott 7
Preston 5
Primus 9
Prince 7
Proctor 9
Prospero 8
Proteus 10
Putnam 7
Pythias 8

Quentin 6
Quinby 9
Quincy 5
Quinn 6

Radburn 10
Radcliffe 8
Radford 9
Rafael 7
Rafe 8
Rainer 6
Raleigh 5
Ralph 1
Ralston 7
Ramiro 5
Ramon 7
Ramsay 6
Randall 5
Randolph 2
Ranger 8
Raoul 5
Raphael 8
Rastus 6
Rathburn 9
Rawlins 7
Ray 1
Raymond 1
Reade 8
Redern 9
Redmond 8
Reed 4
Reese 5

Reeves 7
Reginald 4
Regis 8
Regnard 7
Reid 3
Reinhart 6
Remus 9
Renard 7
Renato 5
Rene 5
Renfred 8
Reuben 3
Rex 3
Reynold 6
Rhett 5
Rhodes 5
Ricardo 3
Richard 1
Richmond 7
Riddell 8
Ridgely 9
Ridgeway 6
Riley 5
Rinaldo 7
Riordan 8
Ritchie 5
Roald 6
Roark 6
Rob 1
Robert 1
Robin 3
Rochester 6
Rod 2
Roderick 5
Rodman 8
Rodney 3
Rodrigo 3
Roger 1
Roland 4
Rolfe 7
Rollin 8
Rollo 8
Roman 7
Romeo 7
Romulo 6

Romulus 5
Ronald 1
Ronan 9
Roric 8
Rory 5
Roscoe 3
Rosmer 10
Ross 3
Rossiter 6
Rosslyn 10
Roswell 9
Rouald 6
Rover 8
Rowan 6
Rowland 7
Roy 1
Royce 6
Ruben 5
Rudolf 5
Rudyard 7
Ruford 9
Rufus 4
Rupert 3
Russell 4
Rutherford 8
Ryan 3

Salvador 3
Sam 1
Samson 6
Samuel 1
Sanborn 8
Sancho 3
Sanders 6
Sandor 7
Sandy 5
Sanford 8
Santiago 7
Sargent 7
Saul 2
Saunders 6
Sawyer 7
Schuyler 5
Scott 3
Sean 3

Searle 8
Seaton 8
Sebastian 4
Sedgwick 8
Selby 9
Selden 7
Selig 8
Selwyn 9
Serge 6
Sergius 9
Seth 2
Seward 7
Seymour 3
Shaw 9
Shawn 4
Sheffield 9
Shelby 7
Sheldon 4
Shelley 5
Shep 1
Shepherd 4
Sheridan 6
Sherlock 4
Sherman 3
Sherry 5
Sherwin 9
Sherwood 7
Shirley 10
Sid 1
Sidney 1
Siebert 8
Sigfried 9
Sigmund 7
Silas 6
Silvester 5
Simeon 6
Simon 4
Sinbad 7
Sinclair 6
Sloane 7
Snyder 6
Sol 4
Solomon 3
Sonny 3
Spencer 4

Stacey 5
Stafford 8
Standish 7
Stanford 6
Stanhope 8
Stanislaus 5
Stanley 1
Stanton 4
Stefan 5
Stefano 7
Stephen 1
Sterling 5
Steven 1
Steward 8
Stewart 2
Stillman 5
Stilwell 7
Stoddard 6
Stuart 2
Sturges 5
Sumner 4
Sutton 9
Sydney 3
Sylvan 7
Sylvester 2
Sylvius 8

Talbot 7
Tate 8
Taylor 6
Ted 1
Telly 6
Terence 3
Terrill 8
Terry 2
Thad 4
Thaddeus 5
Thatcher 8
Thayer 6
Thelonius 10
Theobald 7
Theodore 1
Theron 10
Thomas 1
Thornton 6

Thorpe 8	Ulric 8	Wareham 7	Woodruff 7
Thurman 8	Ulysses 5	Warfield 10	Woodward 6
Thurston 10	Upton 6	Waring 10	Worcester 8
Tiernan 10	Urban 7	Warner 2	Wright 5
Tilden 7	Uriah 8	Warren 1	Wyatt 8
Tilford 10	Ursino 7	Warrick 5	Wylie 8
Tim 1		Warwick 6	Wyman 9
Timon 7	Val 7	Washington 7	Wyndham 10
Timothy 2	Valentine 7	Watson 8	Wynne 6
Tito 8	Valery 8	Wayne 4	Wythe 10
Titus 4	Van 6	Webster 8	
Tobias 6	Vance 5	Weldon 7	Xavier 3
Toby 5	VanDyke 10	Welford 8	Xenos 10
Todd 4	Vanya 5	Wendell 4	Xerxes 10
Tom 1	Varick 10	Werner 6	
Toma 6	Vasily 8	Wescott 6	Yardley 8
Tomas 7	Vaughan 3	Wesley 5	Ymir 10
Tomaso 8	Vergil 8	Weston 7	York 10
Tonio 8	Verlin 10	Whitman 8	Yul 4
Tony 1	Vern 6	Whitney 3	Yuri 10
Torrance 8	Vernon 2	Wickham 10	
Townsend 5	Verrill 9	Wilbert 10	Zaccheus 10
Tracy 4	Victor 1	Wilbur 3	Zachariah 10
Traherne 10	Vincent 1	Wilder 10	Zachary 6
Travis 7	Virgil 8	Wiley 9	Zed 10
Trelawney 8	Vito 3	Wilfred 7	Zeno 10
Tremayne 6	Vivien 6	Wilhelm 4	Zoroaster 8
Tremont 7	Vladimir 5	Will 1	
Trent 8		Willard 4	
Trevelyan 7	Wade 8	Willett 9	
Trevor 5	Wadsworth 6	William 1	
Tristan 4	Wainwright 9	Willis 4	
Tristram 7	Wakefield 7	Willoughby 3	
Truman 8	Walbert 10	Wilson 5	
Tully 7	Walcott 8	Wilton 10	
Tunstan 9	Waldemar 10	Winchell 6	
Turner 7	Walden 6	Winfield 9	
Tybalt 9	Waldo 4	Winfred 5	
Tyler 5	Walford 10	Winslow 5	
Tyndall 6	Walker 5	Winston 2	
Tyrone 3	Wallace 3	Winthrop 2	
Tyson 10	Walt 1	Wolcott 7	
	Walter 1	Wolfe 10	
Ubert 10	Walton 7	Wolfgang 9	
Udall 5	Ward 5	Wood 6	

Abellona 10
Abigail 5
Acacia 10
Ada 2
Adabel 7
Adah 10
Adalia 8
Adaline 4
Adamina 9
Adara 10
Adela 6
Adelaide 3
Adele 1
Adelene 5
Adelia 5
Adelicia 8
Adelina 4
Adelinda 9
Adella 7
Adicia 9
Adina 10
Adione 10
Adolpha 10
Adrena 10
Adriana 7
Adrienne 4
Agatha 2
Agna 10
Agnella 9
Agnes 1
Agola 3
Agustina 10
Aida 5
Aileen 5
Aimee 5
Aina 8
Alameda 7
Alanna 8
Alarice 7
Alatea 8
Alba 8
Alberta 2
Albina 7
Alcena 8
Alcyone 10

Alda 10
Aldabelle 10
Aldora 8
Aleda 6
Alethea 9
Aletta 8
Alexandra 3
Alexis 4
Alfonsine 10
Alfreda 5
Alhena 10
Alianna 7
Alice 1
Alicia 2
Alida 5
Alina 6
Alison 5
Alita 4
Alix 6
Aliza 6
Allegra 4
Allene 4
Alletta 6
Alleyne 7
Alline 5
Allison 5
Allyce 3
Allyn 5
Alma 2
Almedea 10
Almira 10
Alona 8
Aloys 9
Aloysia 9
Alphena 10
Alphonsina 10
Althea 2
Alva 10
Alvina 8
Alvira 9
Alwyn 10
Alyce 2
Alys 7
Alyssa 6
Ama 10

Amabelle 10
Amadis 10
Amala 10
Amalina 10
Amanda 3
Amandine 10
Amapola 10
Amara 10
Amarantha 10
Amaris 9
Amaryllis 8
Amber 6
Ambrosine 10
Amelia 1
Amelie 5
Amethyst 9
Amina 10
Aminta 10
Amity 8
Amoret 10
Amorita 10
Ampara 10
Amy 1
Amybelle 4
Amyntas 10
Ana 7
Anah 10
Anais 8
Anastasia 8
Anatola 8
Ancelin 10
Andrea 3
Andreana 10
Andrita 10
Andromeda 7
Aneta 9
Angel 7
Angela 1
Angelica 5
Angelina 3
Anita 1
Anitra 8
Ann 1
Anna 1
Annabella 1

Annabelle 1
Anne 1
Annetta 1
Annette 1
Annora 7
Annys 10
Anona 10
Anselma 10
Anthea 10
Antoinette 5
Antonia 7
Antonina 7
Apolonia 10
April 4
Ara 10
Arabella 5
Araminta 7
Arbutus 8
Ardeen 9
Ardel 10
Ardelia 10
Ardelis 10
Ardella 10
Ardene 8
Ardetha 10
Ardetta 10
Ardis 10
Ardith 9
Areta 10
Aretina 10
Aretta 10
Ariadne 4
Ariana 7
Ariella 10
Arietta 10
Arita 10
Arleen 3
Arlena 5
Arlene 1
Arleta 7
Arletta 7
Arleyne 10
Arlina 8
Arline 8
Arlis 8

Arlissa 7	Belle 2	Caia 10	Celia 1
Armanda 10	Benedicta 10	Calandra 10	Celina 4
Armantine 10	Benetta 10	Calantha 10	Charis 10
Armeda 10	Benita 7	Calla 10	Charity 3
Armilla 10	Bernadette 5	Calliope 10	Charlene 5
Arminta 10	Bernardina 7	Callista 10	Charlotte 1
Arnoldine 10	Bernetta 6	Calpurnia 10	Charmion 9
Artemis 10	Bernice 1	Camellia 7	Cherry 4
Aselma 10	Berta 3	Camilla 4	Cheryl 3
Asgard 10	Bertha 1	Camille 3	Chiquita 3
Asta 10	Bertina 7	Candace 5	Chita 4
Astarte 10	Beryl 4	Candida 7	Chloe 2
Astred 10	Bess 1	Candy 1	Chloris 4
Astrid 10	Beth 1	Cara 6	Christabel 5
Atalanta 10	Bethana 9	Carin 8	Christel 7
Atalie 7	Bethany 10	Carisa 8	Christie 5
Athene 8	Betsy 1	Carita 9	Christina 2
Atilia 10	Bette 1	Carla 1	Christine 1
Aubertine 10	Bettina 3	Carletta 7	Cicily 1
Audrey 1	Betty 1	Carlotta 3	Cindy 1
Augusta 2	Beulah 3	Carlyn 9	Circe 6
Augustina 4	Bianca 7	Carmela 8	Claire 1
Aurelia 5	Biddy 6	Carmelita 8	Clara 1
Aurora 8	Billie 5	Carmen 1	Clarabelle 1
Ava 3	Bina 10	Carmencita 3	Clarice 6
Aveline 10	Birdie 5	Carmina 7	Clarissa 5
Averil 8	Birgit 10	Carol 1	Claudette 4
Ayleen 4	Blanche 1	Carolina 1	Claudia 1
Aylene 4	Bliss 6	Caroline 1	Claudine 3
Azalea 10	Blondina 10	Carolyn 1	Clematis 8
	Blossom 6	Carrie 5	Clementine 1
Babette 4	Blythe 3	Caryl 4	Cleo 1
Barbara 1	Bonita 6	Cassandra 8	Cleopatra 3
Barbette 8	Bonnie 1	Cassia 10	Clio 4
Barbra 1	Brenda 1	Cassiopeia 8	Clorinda 8
Bathilda 10	Brenna 10	Catalina 7	Clothilde 10
Bathsheba 8	Bride 10	Catherine 1	Clover 10
Batista 10	Bridget 1	Cathleen 2	Clytemnestra 9
Bea 1	Brigette 5	Cathlin 4	Clytie 7
Beatrice 1	Brigit 1	Cecelia 5	Colette 2
Beatrix 1	Bronwen 10	Cecil 7	Colleen 2
Becky 2	Brunella 10	Cecilia 4	Columbine 6
Belinda 3	Brunhilda 4	Cecily 1	Comfort 7
Bella 3	Burdette 8	Celeste 1	Conception 8
Bellanca 10	Burnetta 10	Celestine 1	Concetta 4

Connie 1
Constance 2
Consuela 3
Cora 1
Coral 3
Coralie 3
Cordelia 6
Corella 4
Coretta 3
Corinne 3
Cornelia 2
Corolla 3
Cosette 5
Crispina 9
Cristina 1
Crystal 3
Crystine 5
Cybele 5
Cymbaline 8
Cynara 7
Cynthia 2

Daffodil 5
Dagmar 4
Dahlia 3
Daina 10
Daisy 1
Dale 1
Dallas 10
Damalis 10
Damara 10
Damaris 10
Danella 10
Danielle 1
Danila 10
Danita 9
Daphne 3
Dara 10
Darcy 10
Darlene 1
Daryl 4
Davida 10
Davita 10
Dawn 3
Day 5

Debby 1
Deborah 1
Deirdre 3
Delia 2
Delicia 10
Delilah 3
Della 1
Delora 10
Deloris 6
Delphina 10
Demeter 8
Denice 2
Denise 2
Desdemona 4
Desire 6
Desiree 3
Desmonda 10
Devi 10
Diana 1
Diane 1
Dina 5
Dinah 1
Dione 5
Dionne 3
Dixie 2
Doll 7
Dolly 2
Dolores 1
Donalda 6
Donalee 5
Donella 8
Donna 1
Dora 1
Dorcas 8
Doreen 3
Doretta 3
Dorinda 8
Doris 1
Dorita 4
Dorothea 1
Dorothy 1
Drucilla 3
Duana 10
Dulcinea 7
Dulcy 6

Duretta 5

Earlene 10
Easter 10
Eberta 8
Echo 6
Eda 10
Edana 8
Edeline 6
Edina 8
Edith 1
Edmonda 8
Edna 1
Edris 9
Edwardine 9
Edwina 4
Edythe 2
Effie 3
Egbertine 10
Eileen 1
Eilene 2
Elaine 1
Elane 3
Elberta 8
Eldora 6
Eldoris 7
Eleana 8
Eleanor 1
Electra 5
Elena 3
Eleonora 1
Eleta 6
Eletha 7
Elfreda 10
Elida 10
Elinor 1
Elisa 2
Elisabeth 1
Elise 2
Elissa 3
Eliza 1
Elizabeth 1
Ella 1
Elladora 10
Ellamae 3

Ellen 1
Ellora 7
Elly 1
Ellyn 1
Eloisa 3
Eloise 1
Elsa 1
Elsbet 3
Elsbeth 2
Else 2
Elsie 1
Elspeth 2
Elthea 10
Elvina 10
Elvira 2
Emanuela 8
Emeline 6
Emerald 7
Emilia 1
Emilie 1
Emily 1
Emma 1
Emmaline 4
Emmylou 4
Emogene 7
Emryss 10
Enid 2
Enrica 6
Enys 10
Erianthe 10
Erica 2
Erina 10
Erlina 8
Erlinda 6
Erline 8
Erma 3
Ermelinda 10
Ermengarde 8
Ernestine 5
Ernette 10
Esmeralda 5
Esperanze 7
Essa 10
Essie 3
Estella 5

Estelle 1
Esther 1
Estrella 10
Ethel 1
Etheljean 3
Ethyl 5
Etienette 9
Etta 3
Eudora 5
Eugenia 4
Eugenie 5
Eulalie 10
Eumenida 10
Eunice 1
Euphemie 10
Eurydice 8
Eustacia 9
Eva 1
Evadne 10
Evalina 2
Evaline 2
Evangeline 3
Evanthe 10
Eve 1
Eveleen 4
Eveline 4
Evelyn 1
Eyleen 3

Fae 2
Faith 5
Fannie 1
Fanny 1
Faustine 10
Fawn 8
Fay 1
Faye 1
Fayette 8
Fedora 10
Felice 5
Felicia 6
Felicity 5
Felipa 7
Fenella 9
Fern 7

Fernanda 10
Fidelia 10
Fidelity 10
Fidonia 10
Fifi 3
Filippa 5
Filmena 7
Finella 8
Finna 10
Fiona 6
Flamina 10
Flavia 5
Fleur 8
Flo 2
Flora 1
Florence 1
Floret 10
Florimel 10
Floris 8
Florrie 1
Forestina 10
Fortuna 10
Francena 5
Frances 1
Francesca 3
Francie 1
Francine 2
Freda 3
Frederica 5
Fredonia 6
Freya 10
Frieda 2
Fritzi 6
Fulvia 10

Gabriella 5
Gabrielle 5
Gail 3
Galatea 6
Gale 3
Gardenia 7
Garnet 10
Gavrila 10
Gay 7
Gazella 10

Gemma 10
Geneva 10
Genevieve 2
Georgette 1
Georgia 3
Georgiana 5
Georgina 4
Geraldine 1
Gerardine 10
Gerda 10
Germaine 10
Gertrude 1
Gianina 10
Gidget 3
Gigi 5
Gilberta 10
Gilda 5
Gillian 7
Gina 1
Ginger 5
Giorgina 5
Giovanna 10
Gipsy 7
Giselle 7
Gladine 10
Gladiol 10
Gladys 1
Glenda 1
Glendora 10
Glenna 10
Gloria 1
Gloriana 5
Glory 7
Glyda 10
Glynnis 9
Golda 4
Goldie 2
Goneril 8
Grace 1
Gratiana 10
Greer 8
Greta 2
Gretchen 2
Gretel 2
Griselda 6

Grizel 10
Grushenka 8
Guenevere 5
Guenna 8
Guinevere 2
Gunhild 10
Gussie 3
Gustava 10
Gwen 4
Gwendolen 4
Gweneth 10
Gypsy 7

Hagar 9
Haida 10
Hali 10
Hallie 1
Hanna 7
Hannah 1
Harriet 1
Hattie 1
Hazel 3
Hedda 6
Hedwig 10
Heide 4
Helen 1
Helena 1
Helene 1
Helenka 10
Helga 6
Heloise 2
Hendrika 7
Henrietta 1
Hephzibah 6
Hera 8
Hermia 10
Hermione 5
Hero 7
Hester 5
Hetty 3
Hilary 3
Hilda 1
Hildegarde 3
Holly 5
Honora 9

115

Hope 3
Hortense 2
Hyacinth 10
Hypatia 10

Ianthe 10
Ida 1
Idalah 10
Idalia 10
Idaline 10
Idelle 10
Ilene 10
Ilka 7
Ilona 5
Ilse 6
Imelda 10
Imogen 9
Imogene 5
Ina 5
Ines 6
Inez 4
Inga 5
Ingeborg 6
Inger 7
Ingrid 4
Inis 10
Innocent 7
Ino 10
Io 10
Iola 10
Iolanthe 6
Iona 8
Ionia 10
Iphigenia 7
Irene 1
Irina 3
Iris 1
Irma 1
Irmadel 10
Irmalee 10
Isabel 1
Isabella 1
Isadora 2
Isis 10
Isobel 2

Isolde 10
Ivy 1
Izolda 8

Jacinta 10
Jacobina 10
Jacqueline 1
Jana 10
Jane 1
Janella 10
Janet 1
Janetta 7
Janice 4
Janina 10
Janna 10
Jasmine 4
Jayne 3
Jean 1
Jeanne 1
Jeanette 1
Jehanara 10
Jelena 10
Jemima 2
Jennet 7
Jennifer 1
Jenny 1
Jessamine 8
Jessamy 5
Jesse 2
Jessica 1
Jessie 1
Jewel 5
Jill 1
Jo 4
Joan 1
Joanna 1
Joanne 1
Jocasta 10
Jocelin 4
Jocelyn 3
Joelle 9
Joette 6
Johanna 3
Josefa 7
Josefina 9

Josepha 5
Josephine 1
Joy 3
Joyce 1
Juana 4
Juanita 2
Judith 1
Judy 1
Julia 1
Juliana 5
Julie 1
Juliet 2
June 1
Juno 6
Justine 3

Kaia 10
Kara 10
Karen 1
Karla 2
Katarina 2
Kate 1
Katharine 1
Katherine 1
Kathie 1
Kathleen 1
Kathryn 1
Katie 1
Katrina 5
Kay 2
Kaya 10
Kelda 10
Kelvina 10
Kendra 10
Kerry 5
Kina 10
Kit 4
Kitty 1
Kleantha 10
Komala 10
Kristin 5
Kuni 10

Lael 8
Laetitia 8

Laila 10
Laina 10
Lala 10
Lalita 8
Lambertine 10
Lana 5
Lanessa 10
Lanette 10
Lara 10
Laraine 1
Larissa 7
Laura 1
Laureen 3
Laurel 4
Lauretta 3
Laurette 3
Laverne 1
Lavinia 6
Lea 2
Leah 2
Leanna 8
Leda 10
Lee 1
Leigh 5
Leila 3
Lelia 7
Lena 1
Lenora 1
Lenore 1
Leodora 10
Leola 7
Leona 1
Leonie 9
Leonora 3
Leslie 1
Leta 10
Leticia 3
Letty 1
Liana 7
Liane 8
Libby 1
Lida 6
Lila 3
Lilac 4
Lilian 1

Lilianne 4
Lilith 6
Lillian 1
Lily 1
Lilybelle 3
Lina 2
Linda 1
Linnet 8
Lisa 2
Lisabet 4
Lise 5
Lisette 8
Lisle 5
Livia 7
Liza 3
Lizzie 1
Lois 1
Lola 1
Lolanda 10
Lolita 3
Loraine 1
Lorelei 4
Loretta 2
Lori 8
Lorinda 10
Lorita 7
Lorna 2
Lorraine 1
Lotta 4
Lotte 2
Lottie 1
Lotus 7
Lou 1
Louanne 7
Louella 2
Louisa 1
Louise 1
Luanna 10
Lucasta 8
Lucerne 4
Lucia 4
Lucie 1
Lucilla 7
Lucille 1
Lucinda 5

Lucretia 6
Lucy 1
Ludmila 10
Luisa 2
Lulabel 5
Lulu 1
Lurline 10
Lydia 1
Lynette 6
Lynn 3

Mabel 1
Madalyn 1
Madeleine 1
Madeline 1
Madge 2
Mae 2
Magdalen 3
Maggie 1
Mai 5
Maia 7
Maida 6
Maisie 3
Mala 9
Malina 7
Malvina 8
Mame 3
Mamie 3
Manon 8
Manuela 4
Mara 5
Marcelina 8
Marcella 6
March 7
Marcia 2
Margalo 8
Margaret 1
Marge 1
Margery 1
Margo 2
Margot 3
Margret 1
Marguerite 1
Maria 1
Marian 1

Marianna 1
Marie 1
Marietta 2
Marigold 6
Marijean 10
Marilyn 1
Marina 4
Marion 2
Marjorie 1
Marlene 1
Marna 10
Marta 9
Martha 1
Martine 7
Mary 1
Mary Ann 1
Maryann 1
Marylin 4
Marylou 2
Mathilda 1
Matty 1
Maude 2
Maureen 1
Mavis 3
Maxine 2
May 1
Maya 6
Maybelle 3
Medea 7
Meg 1
Megan 7
Mehitabel 8
Melanie 4
Melicent 6
Melissa 3
Melvina 8
Mercedes 8
Mercy 2
Meredith 6
Merle 6
Merry 1
Meryl 5
Metis 10
Midge 1
Mignon 10

Mignonette 10
Miguela 10
Mila 10
Mildred 1
Millicent 1
Millie 1
Mimi 4
Minerva 5
Minetta 7
Minna 4
Minnie 1
Mione 10
Mira 5
Mirabel 6
Miranda 2
Miriam 1
Miriamne 3
Moina 10
Moira 5
Mollie 1
Molly 1
Mona 3
Monica 2
Mora 9
Morgana 10
Moria 8
Muriel 1
Myra 1
Myrna 1
Myrrh 10
Myrtle 2

Nada 10
Nadia 7
Nadine 5
Naida 9
Nan 1
Nana 3
Nancy 1
Nanette 3
Nanine 8
Naomi 1
Nara 10
Narcissa 10
Natalia 7

117

Natalie 2
Natasha 8
Nell 1
Nella 6
Nellie 1
Nelly 1
Nerice 10
Nerine 10
Nerissa 7
Nerita 10
Neroli 10
Netta 10
Nettie 1
Neva 8
Nicole 2
Nicolette 3
Nieta 10
Nina 1
Ninon 6
Nita 5
Noelle 5
Nola 10
Nona 8
Nora 1
Norah 1
Norberta 9
Nordica 10
Noria 10
Norine 10
Norma 1
Nydia 6
Nyssa 10

Octavia 10
Odaris 10
Odelette 10
Odelia 6
Odella 8
Odessa 10
Odette 6
Odile 10
Odina 10
Olga 1
Olinda 10
Olita 10

Olive 2
Olivia 1
Olympia 7
Omphale 10
Ona 5
Ondine 10
Onida 10
Onora 10
Oonagh 10
Opal 4
Ophelia 1
Orabelle 10
Oralia 10
Ordelle 10
Orela 10
Orette 10
Oriana 10
Orinda 10
Orita 10
Ottilie 3
Ouida 10
Oya 10

Pamela 1
Pandora 1
Pansy 1
Paola 7
Parmelia 10
Parthenia 10
Pat 1
Patience 7
Patricia 1
Patsy 1
Patty 1
Paula 2
Paulette 3
Pauline 1
Pavita 10
Peace 10
Pearl 1
Peg 1
Peggy 1
Penelope 4
Peony 7
Pepita 10

Perdita 10
Petra 10
Petronella 10
Petrova 10
Petunia 10
Phebe 5
Phedre 10
Philemena 7
Philippa 4
Phoebe 5
Phyllis 1
Pierrette 7
Pilar 10
Pippa 8
Polly 1
Pollyanna 1
Poppy 3
Portia 5
Priscilla 1
Prudence 1
Prunella 8
Psyche 10

Queena 5
Queenie 2

Rachel 4
Rae 2
Raina 8
Ramona 5
Rana 10
Raymonda 3
Reba 3
Rebecca 1
Regan 7
Regina 3
Reina 10
Renata 10
Renee 4
Reva 10
Rhea 1
Rheta 10
Rhoda 1
Rina 10
Rita 1

Roberta 1
Robin 5
Robina 10
Romelda 10
Rona 10
Ronalda 10
Ronnie 2
Rosa 2
Rosabel 2
Rosalie 1
Rosalind 2
Rosamond 2
Rosanne 6
Rose 1
Rosemarie 1
Rosemary 1
Rosetta 6
Rosina 10
Rosita 2
Roslyn 1
Rowena 5
Roxanne 4
Roxie 5
Rozelle 10
Ruana 10
Ruby 4
Rucita 5
Ruella 10
Ruth 1

Sabina 6
Sabrina 5
Sacha 10
Sada 6
Sadie 1
Saida 10
Sal 1
Sally 1
Salome 4
Samantha 3
Samara 10
Sandra 1
Santa 7
Sara 1
Sarah 1

Sarita 10
Sascha 6
Scarlett 5
Selena 7
Selina 4
Selma 2
Semele 10
Serafina 10
Serena 10
Shan 10
Sharon 3
Sheelagh 4
Sheila 1
Sherrill 10
Shirley 1
Sibyl 5
Sidonia 3
Signe 4
Sigrid 5
Silene 10
Silvia 1
Siobhan 7
Sofia 4
Sonia 1
Sonja 1
Sonya 1
Sophie 1
Stacy 1
Star 10
Stella 1
Stephanie 1
Sue 1
Suni 10
Susan 1
Susanna 1
Susanne 1
Susette 1
Susie 1
Suzette 1
Swanhilda 10
Sybil 1
Sylvia 1

Tabitha 4
Taffy 5

Tallulah 6
Tamar 10
Tamara 4
Tammy 1
Tara 5
Teresa 1
Terese 1
Tess 1
Tessa 1
Thea 2
Thelma 1
Theodora 1
Theodosia 8
Theresa 1
Thetis 10
Thisbe 6
Thomasina 10
Tilda 10
Till 1
Tillie 1
Timothea 7
Tina 6
Titania 5
Toni 4
Tonia 8
Tracy 6
Tricia 5
Trilby 10
Trina 5
Trixie 1
Trudie 1

Ula 10
Una 5
Undine 10
Urania 10
Uriana 10
Ursa 7
Ursula 1

Valentina 9
Valerie 6
Valora 10
Vanessa 1
Varenka 10

Varina 10
Varinka 10
Varvara 10
Vasilia 10
Veda 6
Veleda 10
Veleva 10
Velia 10
Velika 10
Velma 1
Venetia 10
Venita 10
Vera 1
Verbena 10
Verena 10
Vergilia 10
Verla 10
Verlyn 10
Verna 10
Vernadine 10
Verne 10
Vernette 10
Verona 6
Veronica 1
Veronique 5
Vesta 10
Veva 10
Vevila 10
Vickie 2
Victoria 1
Vida 3
Vidette 5
Villa 10
Villette 10
Vilma 10
Vina 10
Vincentia 10
Viola 1
Violet 1
Violetta 1
Virgilia 1
Virginia 1
Vita 10
Vivian 1
Viviana 8

Vivianne 3

Wanda 1
Wannetta 8
Wendy 10
Wilhelmina 3
Willa 5
Winifred 1
Winnie 1
Winona 6
Wynette 10
Wynne 5

Xanthe 10
Xanthippe 10
Xene 10
Xenia 10
Xenisma 10
Ximena 10
Xylia 10
Xylina 10
Xylona 10
Xylopala 10
Xylophila 10
Xylota 10

Yarmilla 10
Yolanda 1
Ysolde 10
Yvette 1
Yvonne 1

Zada 10
Zaidee 10
Zamora 10
Zara 10
Zelda 2
Zelina 10
Zella 10
Zelma 10
Zelota 10
Zena 4
Zenia 10
Zenobia 10
Zeora 10

Categories—Girls' Names—Z

Zepha 10
Zilia 10
Zinnia 7
Ziona 10
Zoe 5

Zohra 10
Zola 10
Zona 10
Zora 10
Zorabel 10

Zorah 10
Zorana 10
Zorna 10
Zula 10
Zuleika 10

Zulena 10
Zulota 10
Zyma 10

Categories—Land Animals— Mammals —A —D

Aardvark 4
Aardwolf 10
Addax 7
Agouti 9
Ai 9
Alpaca 7
Ammon 10
Anoa 10
Ant Bear 7
Anteater 3
Antelope 2
Aoudad 10
Ape 1
Arctic Fox 9
Argali 10
Ariel 10
Armadillo 4
Ass 1
Axis Deer 9
Aye-Aye 10

Babirussa 10
Baboon 1
Badger 5
Bamboo Bat 10
Bamboo Rat 10
Bandicoot 9
Barbary Ape 3
Bat 1
Bear 1
Beaver 2
Beisa Oryx 10

Bharal 10
Bighorn 8
Binturong 10
Bison 3
Blackbuck 7
Blesbok 10
Blue Bull 10
Boar 3
Bobac 10
Bobcat 2
Bohor Reedbuck 10
Bongo 10
Bontebok 10
Brocket 10
Buck 4
Buffalo 1
Bull 1
Burro 4
Bush Baby 8
Bushbuck 9
Bush Pig 8

Cacomistle 10
Camel 1
Capybara 7
Carabao 10
Caracal 10
Caribou 6
Castor 10
Cat 1
Catamount 10
Cavy 10

Cayuse 10
Chacma 10
Chamois 10
Cheetah 5
Chevrotain 10
Chickaree 10
Chimpanzee 1
Chinchilla 6
Chipmunk 3
Chital 10
Civet 8
Coati 8
Colugo 10
Cony 10
Cottontail 3
Cougar 4
Cow 1
Coyote 1
Coypu 10
Cus-Cus 10

Daman 10
Deer 1
Desman 10
Dhole 10
Dik-Dik 10
Dingo 5
Dog 1
Donkey 1
Dormouse 6
Douc 10
Drill 10

Dromedary 4
Duikerbok 10

Echidna 10
Eland 8
Elephant 1
Elephant Seal 8
Elephant Shrew 10
Elk 2
Ermine 5
Eyra 10

Fennec 9
Ferret 6
Fisher 8
Fitch 10
Flying Fox 10
Flying Lemur 8
Flying Squirrel 6
Foussa 10
Foumart 10
Fox 1
Fox Squirrel 8

Galago 10
Gaur 10
Gayal 10
Gazelle 5
Gemsbok 10
Genet 10
Gerbil 2
Gibbon 3
Giraffe 1
Glutton 10
Gnu 3
Goat 1
Goat Antelope 10
Gopher 3
Goral 10
Gorilla 1
Grison 10
Grivet 10
Ground Hog 2
Ground Squirrel 10
Guanaco 10

Guenon 10
Guereza 10
Guinea Pig 2

Hamadryad 10
Hamster 3
Hamster Mole 8
Hare 1
Hart 7
Hartebeest 9
Hedgehog 7
Hinny 10
Hippopotamus 1
Hog 1
Hog Badger 10
Hog Deer 9
Honey Bear 4
Honey Dog 8
Hoolock 10
Horse 1
Hound 1
Howler Monkey 7
Huanaco 10
Hutia 10
Hyena 2
Hyrax 10

Ibex 6
Ichneumon 10
Impala 6

Jackal 4
Jackass 2
Jack Rabbit 3
Jaguar 2
Jaguarundi 10
Javali 10
Jerboa 10

Kalong 10
Kangaroo 1
Kangaroo Mouse 8
Kangaroo Rat 8
Karakul 8
Kiang 10

Kinkajou 9
Klipspringer 10
Koala 5
Kob 10
Kudu 10

Lamb 1
Langur 10
Leaf Monkey 9
Lemming 6
Lemming Mouse 10
Lemur 5
Leopard 1
Leopard Seal 7
Linsang 10
Lion 1
Llama 2
Loris 10
Lynx 4

Macaque 10
Man 3
Mandrill 6
Mangabey 9
Manul 10
Maral Stag 10
Mare 5
Margay 7
Markhor 10
Marmoset 7
Marmot 8
Marsh Buck 7
Marsh Deer 7
Marten 5
Meerkat 8
Mink 2
Mole 3
Mole Lemming 10
Money Mouse 10
Mongoose 6
Monkey 1
Moonrat 10
Moose 1
Mouflon 10
Mountain Beaver 10

Mountain Goat 3
Mountain Lion 2
Mouse 1
Mule 1
Mule Deer 10
Muntjak 10
Musk Ox 6
Muskrat 3
Musquash 10
Mustang 2

Nilgai 10
Noctule 10
Nutria 6
Nyala 10

Ocelot 2
Okapi 7
Onager 10
Opossum 2
Orangutan 2
Oribi 10
Oryx 10
Otter 2
Ounce 10
Owl Monkey 10
Ox 1

Paca 10
Painter 10
Pallah 10
Pampas Deer 10
Panda 1
Pangolin 9
Panolia Deer 10
Panther 1
Peba 10
Peccary 8
Pekan 10
Phalanger 10
Pichiciago 10
Pig 1
Pig Deer 10
Pika 10
Platypus 6
Pocket Gopher 10

Pocket Mouse 10
Polar Bear 2
Polecat 3
Pongo 10
Pony 1
Porcupine 1
Possum 2
Potto 10
Prairie Dog 5
Pronghorn 10
Puma 2
Pygmy Buffalo 10

Rabbit 1
Rabbit Rat 10
Raccoon 1
Raccoon Dog 10
Ram 5
Rasse 10
Rat 1
Rat Kangaroo 10
Ratel 10
Red Deer 6
Reedbuck 10
Reindeer 1
Rhesus Monkey 10
Rhinoceros 2
Rice Rat 10
Roan Antelope 10
Rocky Mountain
  Goat 6
Roe Deer 10

Sable 2
Saiga 10
Saki 10
Sambar 10
Sapajou 10
Sassaby 10
Sea Lion 5
Seal 2
Seladang 10
Serow 10
Serval 10
Sewellel 10

Sheep 1
Sheep Cow 10
Sheep Deer 10
Shetland Pony 3
Shrew 4
Shrew Mole 10
Shrew Mouse 10
Siamang 7
Skunk 1
Sloth 5
Sow 7
Spider Monkey 6
Spiny Anteater 7
Springbok 9
Springhaas 10
Squirrel 1
Squirrel Monkey 10
Stag 1
Steer 1
Steinbok 8
Stoat 7
Suni 10
Suricate 10
Suslik 10
Swine 3

Tahr 10
Takin 10
Talapoin 10
Tamandua 10
Tamarau 10
Tamarin 10
Tapir 5
Tarpan 10
Tarsier 10
Tasmanian Devil 7
Tayra 10
Tenrec 8
Thylacine 10
Tiger 1
Titi 10
Tree Shrew 10
Tuco Tuco 10

Unau 10
Urial 10

Vampire Bat 5
Vervet 10
Vicuña 7
Viscacha 10
Vole 8

Wallaby 4
Wallaroo 10
Walrus 1
Wanderoo 10
Wapiti 8
Warrigal 10
Warthog 5

Waterbuck 8
Water Buffalo 4
Water Hog 7
Water Rat 5
Weasel 2
Weasel Cat 5
Wild Ass 5
Wild Boar 3
Wildcat 2
Wildebeest 8
Wisent 10
Wolf 1
Wolverine 5

Wombat 5
Woodchuck 2

Yak 2
Yapok 10

Zebra 2
Zebra Duiker 10
Zebra Mongoose 10
Zebu 10
Zibet 10
Zoril 10

Categories—Food Plants —A –C

Acorn squash 6
Akee 10
Alecost 10
Alligator pear 6
Allspice 7
Almond 2
Alpine
   strawberry 10
Amarelle 10
Angelica 9
Anise 7
Apple 1
Apricot 2
Arrowroot 8
Artichoke 3
Asparagus 1
Asparagus pea 9
Aubergine 10
Avocado 2

Balm 10
Balsam pear 10
Bambarra
   groundnut 10

Bamboo shoots 8
Banana 1
Baobab 10
Barberry 8
Barley 1
Basil 2
Bayberry 5
Bay leaf 3
Beach plum 8
Bean 1
Beet 1
Bilberry 5
Blackberry 2
Black-eyed pea 6
Black gram 10
Black mustard 10
Black salsify 10
Blackthorn 10
Black walnut 10
Bladder cherry 10
Blewits 10
Blood orange 7
Blueberry 1
Borage 9

Boysenberry 6
Brazil nut 3
Breadfruit 7
Broad bean 7
Broccoli 2
Brussels sprouts 2
Buckwheat 4
Bullace 10
Burnet 10
Butter bean 8
Butternut 6
Butternut squash 7

Cabbage 1
Cabbage
   palmetto 10
Cacao 4
Calamondin 10
Caltrop 10
Camomile 6
Cantaloupe 1
Cape
   gooseberry 10
Capers 7

Carambola 10
Caraway 5
Cardamom 9
Cardoon 10
Carrageen 10
Carrot 1
Cashew nut 3
Cassava 8
Cauliflower 2
Celeriac 10
Celery 2
Celtuce 9
Cep 10
Ceriman 10
Chanterelle 10
Chard 4
Cherimoya 10
Cherry 1
Cherry plum 4
Cherry tomato 3
Chervil 6
Chestnut 3
Chick pea 7
Chicory 6
Chili pepper 5
Chinese cabbage 10
Chinese chives 10
Chinese lantern
   plant 10
Chinese water
   chestnut 5
Chives 5
Cicely 10
Cinnamon 3
Cintrange 10
Citron 7
Clementine 9
Cloudberry 9
Cloves 3
Coconut 1
Coffee 1
Collard 8
Comfrey 10
Coralberry 9
Coriander 7

Corn 1
Costmary 10
Courgette 10
Cowberry 8
Cowpea 10
Crabapple 5
Cranberry 2
Cranshaw melon 6
Cress 6
Crookneck
   squash 9
Cucumber 2
Currant 4
Cuscus 10
Cushaw 10
Custard apple 7

Damson 10
Dandelion 2
Dasheen 10
Date 3
Dewberry 8
Dill 6
Dulse 10
Durian 10
Durra 8

Eddoes 10
Eggplant 3
Elderberry 5
Endive 5
Escarole 6

Fennel 9
Fenugreek 10
Fig 4
Filbert 4
Finocchio 8
Florence fennel 10

Garlic 3
Gean 10
Gherkin 7
Ginger 2
Goa bean 10

Good King
   Henry 10
Gooseberry 6
Granadilla 8
Grape 1
Grapefruit 2
Great nettle 10
Green gram 10
Ground cherry 8
Guava 5
Guinea corn 8
Gumbo 8

Hackberry 8
Haw 10
Hazelnut 5
Honeydew
   melon 3
Hop 8
Horehound 7
Horse-radish 7
Huckleberry 3
Husk tomato 8
Hyacinth bean 10
Hyssop 10

Ilama 10
Indian corn 6
Indian cress 8
Indian currant 9
Indian fig 10
Indian lettuce 10
Indian rice 10

Jack bean 8
Jack-fruit 7
Japanese
   persimmon 10
Japanese
   quince 10
Japan pepper 10
Jersualem
   artichoke 9
Juniper berry 8

Kale 9
Kava 8
Kidney bean 2
Kiwi 7
Kohlrabi 10
Kumquat 6

Lablab 10
Laver 10
Leek 6
Lemon 1
Lentil 3
Lettuce 1
Lichee nut 8
Licorice 4
Lima bean 1
Lime 3
Loganberry 7
Loquat 10
Lotus 10
Lovage 10

Macadamia nut 10
Mace 7
Maize 1
Malabar spinach 10
Mandarin
  orange 7
Mangel-wurzel 10
Mango 5
Mangosteen 10
Manioc 10
Marjoram 5
Marrow 10
Marshmallow 6
Mat bean 10
Maté 10
Maypop 8
Medlar 10
Melon 1
Mercury 10
Mexican apple 10
Mexican black
  bean 10

Mexican ground
  cherry 10
Millet 9
Mint 1
Morel 10
Morello 10
Moreton Bay
  chestnut 10
Moth bean 10
Mulberry 4
Mung bean 10
Mushroom 2
Muskmelon 4
Mustard 1

Navy bean 7
Nectarine 5
New Zealand
  spinach 10
Niger seed 10
Nutmeg 5

Oats 3
Oca 10
Oil palm 10
Okra 5
Olive 2
Onion 1
Orache 10
Orange 1
Oyster plant 10

Palmyra palm 10
Papaya 6
Parsley 3
Parsnip 6
Passion fruit 10
Pawpaw 9
Pea 1
Peach 1
Peanut 3
Pear 1
Pecan 4
Pepper 4

Peppermint 5
Persimmon 6
Pillepesara 10
Pimento 8
Pineapple 1
Pine kernels 8
Pistachio 5
Plantain 9
Plum 1
Plum tomato 6
Pomegranate 7
Pomelo 10
Popcorn 1
Potato 1
Prune 1
Pumpkin 1

Quandong 10
Queensland
  nut 10
Quince 5

Radish 1
Raisin 1
Rambutan 10
Rape 10
Raspberry 2
Red currant 8
Rhubarb 4
Rice 1
Rocambole 10
Rocket 10
Romaine 5
Rose hips 6
Rosemary 5
Rowan 10
Rutabaga 10
Rye 2

Saber bean 9
Safflower 7
Saffron 8
Sage 5
Sago 10
Salsify 10

Samphire 10
Sand leek 10
Sapodilla
    plum 10
Sarsaparilla 9
Savory 8
Scallion 5
Scorzonera 10
Scotch lovage 10
Sea grape 10
Sea kale 10
Serviceberry 10
Sesame 5
Shaddock 10
Shallot 7
Shea-butter
    nut 10
Sloe 10
Sorghum 8
Sorrel 9
Soursop 10
Southernwood 10
Soya 7
Soybean 4
Spearmint 3
Spinach 1
Squash 3
Stinging nettle 6
Strawberry 1

Strawberry
    tomato 10
Stringbean 1
Sugar apple 7
Sugar beet 6
Sugarberry 8
Sugar cane 5
Sunflower 3
Swedish
    turnip 10
Sweet potato 1
Sweetsop 10
Sword bean 9

Tamarind 8
Tangelo 5
Tangerine 2
Tansy 10
Tapioca 5
Taro 7
Tarragon 6
Tea 3
Teff 9
Tepary bean 10
Thyme 3
Tomatillo 10
Tomato 1
Truffle 10
Turmeric 10
Turnip 2

Ugli 10

Vanilla 1
Vegetable
    marrow 10
Vetch 10

Walnut 1
Water chestnut 7
Watercress 5
Watermelon 1
Wheat 1
Whortleberry 10
Wild date
    palm 10
Wild rice 5
Wild spikenard 10
Wineberry 10
Winter cherry 10
Winter cress 8
Winter melon 10
Winter
    purslane 10
Witloof 9
Wormwood 9

Yam 3

Zucchini 6

INDEX